THE GUIDE TO COMMUNAL LIVING

DIGGERS
-&-
DREAMERS

94/95

EDITED BY

CHRIS COATES

JONATHAN HOW

LEE JONES

WILLIAM MORRIS

ANDY WOOD

A **Communes Network** Publication

©
Communes Network
1993

First published
1993
Communes Network
care of
Redfield Community
Winslow
Buckinghamshire
MK18 3LZ

ISBN
0 9514945 2 X
Paperback

Printing (contents)
RAP Ltd
201 Spotland Road
Rochdale
OL12 7AF
Printing (cover)
Lithosphere Printing
Co-operative Ltd
82/90 Queensland Rd
London
N7 7AW
Typesetting and Layout
Jonathan How
Redfield
Winslow
Buckinghamshire
MK18 3LZ

Cover photograph: *Houses at Lightmoor*

Photographic credits (where known)
Chris Coates: pages 35,37, 46 and 98
Roger Hallam: page 94
Jonathan How: cover
Bill Metcalf: pages 14, 16, 17 and 18

Contents

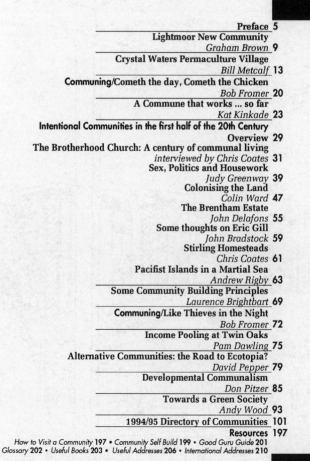

Preface

*"You can sit down and write a prescription for a utopia
but then what the hell? You can't legislate humanism. You
can't make people be nice to each other. You can't even
hardly trick them into it. They'll do it voluntarily if you
take the pressure off them but that costs money. And
who's got the money? People who don't give a damn. How
can you hope? You're naïve if you hope."*

Frank Zappa, May 1993

Here we are, well into the so-called "caring
nineties" - the caring nineties of mass
unemployment, permanent recession,
soft-focus Thatcherism, global warming,
new environmental disasters announced
daily, wars in Europe, Africa, Asia ...

How can we hope?

Widespread disillusion with conventional politics,
and political parties, as a source of hope is leading
more and more people to turn to small scale community initiatives (community in the widest sense of the
word). These initiatives are building on the successes
(and learning from the failures) of the various experiments in community politics that started in the
1970s. Of those experiments intentional communities - or communes as they were called then - were
perhaps some of the higher profile experiments offering perscriptions of utopia, due mainly to media
interest in sex, drugs and wholemeal rolls. Can the
communes of the seventies (and before) that have
survived through the Thatcherite counter-revolution-
ary years be seen as harbingers of hope? The truth is
that only the proverbial 'time will tell'. In the meantime, however, David Pepper, Don Pitzer and Andy
Wood in their articles: 'The Road to Ecotopia?',

**Well,
how *can* we
hope?**

'Developmental Communalism' and 'Towards a Green Society', give pointers to the place of intentional communities in the cultivation of a practical utopian future.

Elsewhere in the book you will find the nitty gritty of communal life. From the inspirational to the day-to-day mundane details, as in Kat Kinkade and Pam Dawling's descriptions of Twin Oaks. From the historical perspective of the section on 'Intentional Comunities in the first half of the Twentieth Century', with feature articles by Colin Ward, Judy Greenway, John Delafons and Andrew Rigby; to the humourous satires on modern communal life by Bob Fromer.

> **How can you hope? You're naïve if you hope.**

In the 'Directory' section you will find details of a large cross section of intentional communities in Britain - most of whom are on the look-out for new members. It is estimated that for every listed group there are between four and ten other groups who wish to remain anonymous - giving a sizeable minority of people quietly getting on with their communal lives. Interestingly there are a number of new comunities forming that are of the local network/small village/sustainable living system type that were outlined by Simon Poulter and Jonathan How in their article 'New Communities' in *Diggers and Dreamers 92/93*.

You will find further practical information in the 'Resources' section at the back of the book on such subjects as 'How to Visit a Community', 'Community Self-Build' and 'Useful Addresses' both in Britain and abroad.

We have an ongoing debate amongst ourselves about what constitutes an "intentional community" or "commune", or whatever other word any given group chooses to describe itself. Our definitions,

when we do manage to arrive at any, are pleasantly flexible and inclusive as there are really as many views on the subject as there are people involved in "doing it". We believe that communal living has a part to play in the creation of a better society and invite you to join us and add your own particular views to the vision.

"The whole blessed thing is an obstacle race for happiness."

Edward Carpenter. Quoted in The New Horizon in Love and Life *by Edith Lees (1921)*

The whole blessed thing is an obstacle race for happiness.

Acknowledgements

Once again we would like to thank all the groups who provided (even more) entries for the 'Directory' section - it's really fascinating to read them as they come in. Thanks also to all those who have contributed articles (including those that were not ultimately used) and especially to Andrew Rigby for complying with our, apparently, endless demands. We've shared a lot of the text entry between us but Michelle Lawson also made a substantial contribution. The communities at People in Common, Bamford and Redfield have provided venues for our meetings and also electricity, space, food and good atmospheres. Richard Kelley proved that *Windows* was good for something and Simon Poulter and Julie Penfold put up with us endlessly using their Apple File Exchange to get back into *Macintosh* format! We'd also like to thank all those readers of the previous editions who have given feedback - we hope that even more readers will let us know what they think by filling out the post-paid card at the end of the book and sending it back to us.

Lightmoor New Community

GRAHAM BROWN

It all began, quite fittingly, on New Year's day when Dr Tony Gibson, Projects Officer for the *Town and Country Planning Association* (*TCPA*), looked out on a 22 acre site in the backwaters of Telford new town. He had found the location for his experiment in community development, soon he would find the money and, more importantly, the people. Since that day in 1984 the Lightmoor New Community has evolved into a self built, self reliant village. Whilst the achievements of the 14 households cannot be underestimated, it has not been accomplished without cost and a certain amount of compromise.

The community was probably as much a product of the Thatcher years as was the Yuppie. Whilst it was certainly driven initially by a sense of enterprise, it sought to detach itself from many aspects of the developing moral and social climate. To those interested in the scheme the idea needed little selling. There was a general desire to avoid the mistakes of a fragmenting society based on materialism and waste; a society that was giving way to urban decay and rising crime.

The householders encompass a wide diversity of skills and professions, consequently their reasons for involvement were various. Andy Murray, a computer software designer, was looking for a "small, supportive community which took responsibility for community life and the environment." Those same twin values of co-operation and environmental awareness are echoed elsewhere. For Paul Radcliffe, a mechanic and his wife Mahdu, who worked closely with Dr Gibson on his community initiatives, the motivation was obvious: "The important aspects for

The story of the Town and Country Planning Association's Third Garden City Plan and the failure of the Greentown group to implement it in Milton Keynes was featured in D&D 92/93. The story of success in Telford is taken up by Graham Brown who describes the Lightmoor Project.

us are sharing responsibility and decision making for our environment with our neighbours."

For others there was the opportunity to build workshops and enjoy home-based e m p l o y m e n t, avoiding the dreaded gridlock scenario of rush hour traffic. Simon Harper found the prospect irresistible: "Lightmoor has given me the opportunity to establish my own business, designing and making high quality furniture from homegrown hardwood."

There existed a consensus amongst the residents that the community offered an alternative to suburban and inner city life - often seen as fast, furious, wasteful and alienating. Here they had control over their immediate environment, and the spirit of community was bolstered by the need for all to 'muck in', developing the infrastructure. Residents drove maniacally around the site in their JCB, laying down the water pipeline and electric cables and there was a growing sense of achievement as amenities came on line. The septic tank and treatment plant provided the community with its own recycling sewage system.

....

there was a growing sense of achievement as amenities came on line

....

The various skills of the community, which included architects, planners, bricklayers, civil engineers and furniture designers, was harnessed to raise the brick and timber framed houses. The residents set up their own company to assist the financing of the project and the idea of 'sweat equity' was put into practice. This is an arrangement which allows the house purchaser to use their own skills and labour to help meet borrowing requirements. As Dr Gibson was quick to point out, "It's nothing new. But you have to go back a couple of generations to the wartime blitz to find everyone taking mutual dependence for granted."

Following *The Times/RIBA* award for Community Enterprise in 1987, and a visit from its patron, Prince Charles soon after, the community was thrust into the glare of publicity. The residents began to realise the significance of the project, but also became aware of the onus on them to succeed. The press drew comparisons with the Garden Cities pioneered by Ebenezer Howard at the beginning of the century. They were cast as pioneers, setting out on a new lifestyle that could become a model for us all. However, behind the soundbites were individuals who were beginning to suffer from the strain of it all.

The community, for all its self sufficiency, was still very much part of the wider society. Consequently it was not impervious to the ravages of recession and marital break up. A number of households have been hit by unemployment. Moreover, the process of building your own home, especially on those freezing winter nights with the family packed like sardines into a second hand caravan, provides its own unique pressures. For some it has been too much.

often it has been a case of making it up as we went along

For the community as a whole there has been no real blueprint to work to, and often it has been a case of making it up as we went along. Where there is collaboration between individuals there is also inevitably conflict. The regular meetings of a 'vibes' group went some way to smoothing out grievances. Bureaucratic delays in their dealings with the housing association and the building society, who provided most of the financial backing, have been further sources of frustration. Perhaps as a result of these shared hardships, the community itself has been strengthened, but it has lost some of its idealism and vision along the way.

Certainly a number of the initiatives originally planned have failed to come to fruition - the conversion of the Poplars building into a resource centre; the youth workshop on site has barely fulfilled its potential; there is still a great deal of landscaping of the plots and the village green to be carried out. Yet despite the shortfalls and pressures of the project there is little sign of disillusion amongst the residents, merely a realignment of values.

Inevitably once the communal tasks of infrastructure and house building were complete, the impetus for co-operation was given over to more individual concerns. The question for the community is - where does it go from here? Perhaps it views itself as being less distant now from a society which is starting to value the environment and which is putting more emphasis on quality of life, rather than material acquisition. There is danger of course that with the community members comfortably ensconced in their cosy homes they will lose their pioneering edge. There is no doubting the achievement so far. The choice now lies between consolidation of that achievement or striving for new, more ambitious goals.

Graham Brown studied English at Lancaster University where he was editor of the College Magazine. After graduating in 1987 he lived in London for five years working as a Sales Executive. In 1992 he returned to the Midlands and is currently writing freelance as well as studying Marketing. His parents were amongst the first members of the Lightmoor Project and have been able to monitor its progress since 1984.

Crystal Waters Permaculture Village: new age social planning ... or rural suburbia?

BILL
METCALF

C rystal Waters Permaculture Village is an intentional community, about 150 kilometres (100 miles) north of Brisbane, Australia. It started as a typical, directionless, rural, secular alternative lifestyle community in 1978. By 1986, through dissent and a lack of direction, the original community of 40-50 people collapsed. The community was reformed using 'Group Titles' as a legal mechanism, and was promoted in the alternative as well as main stream media as being devoted to the ideals of permaculture. The work was undertaken by four people, all with permaculture and community development experience, who were paid a salary out of the eventual sale of shares. These people were known as 'the planners'.

Permaculture has received considerable interest and enthusiasm within the worldwide intentional community movement. Bill Mollison, from Tasmania, developed permaculture simply as "designed agriculture"[1], but enthusiasts around the world have broadened the scope to become an overall approach to environmental and social design and management. Permaculture at Crystal Waters was defined by the planners as:

A permanent, self sustaining system of agriculture, adaptable to both urban and rural situations designed to produce an efficient, low maintenance, optimally productive integration of trees, plants, animals, structures and human activities within specific environments.[2]

In other words, permaculture was seen as providing a model on which a fully planned, 'utopian' com-

Australian
Permaculture
Village Crystal
Waters sounds
like Heaven on
Earth but what
is it really like?

munity could be planned and developed. Crystal Waters Permaculture Village was the first, and is still the largest of this kind of community in the world, so its success is of great interest within the global intentional community movement.

Group Titles is a legal structure similar to that applying to strata-titles in large apartment or condominium buildings, where individuals own small areas (such as one's flat), with ownership of the remaining area and all infrastructure invested in the group as a corporation, usually known as 'the Body Corporate'.

Crystal Waters Permaculture Village covers 259 hectares (640 acres) with 1 kilometre (1/2 mile) frontage to the Mary River. 83 shares were sold for $21,000 (£8,000) each, giving the owner freehold title to a homesite of about 0.5 hectares (1 acre). 5-8 homesites are grouped into a hamlet. The remaining land, including about 15 hectares of river flats as well as heavily forested hills, is owned in common. All roads, bridges, the water and electricity supply, and other community infrastructure, is communally owned and is managed by the Body Corporate, being paid for by a levy or tax on each share. Members decide upon by-laws or 'covenants' which are then legally enforceable by the Body Corporate. In other words, Crystal Waters operates almost exactly as its own local government or municipality. This legal structure facilitates group control over the environment, by allowing (for instance) the banning of cats and dogs (which are a threat to native fauna), control over what trees are planted or cut down, and

[1]MOLLISON, B (1979) *Permaculture Two* Tagari Books, Tagar

[2]*Crystal Waters Permaculture Village Owner's Manual* (1988).

what building materials and practices are acceptable.[3]

Members were recruited through advertisements placed in new-age and alternative publications. The Crystal Waters' planners produced a number of professional brochures and documents extolling the virtues of 'the village' as a planning ideal. The imagery was derived from European mythology as well as the village community ideas of anarchists such as Kropotkin. The planners travelled to other parts of Australia where they talked of their vision of a 'permaculture village'. This process was remarkably successful.

Prospective purchasers, after touring the property, were interviewed by one of the planners, told about the covenants which already applied, and then, if still interested, were allowed to buy a share. The people attracted to Crystal Waters were similar to other intentional community members in Australia[4], being comparatively well educated, often from middle class, professional backgrounds, between 30-50 years of age, and having environmental and social concerns and motivations.[5]

Houses have been built on more than half the blocks and there is now a resident population of over 100 people (including children). Members offer a programme of educational courses ranging from permaculture to personal growth. There is accommodation for 24 course attendees and visitors in a purpose-built, community owned dormitory, and another 20-30 in caravans and tents. A new, communal kitchen and dining area was completed in early 1993, further enhancing the community's ability to generate income through offering 'new age' courses to the general public.

It is a common observation by researchers, as well as participants within the intentional community movement, that religious and spiritual groups often work better, and last longer, than secular groups. Researchers credit this greater success not to the features of any particular belief system, but to the sharing of a common set of beliefs. In other words, it matters far less in what intentional community members believe, than that they share a common belief system or ideology. Christian and Buddhist communes work well not because of Christianity or Buddhism *per se*, but because all members share the same set of beliefs or 'paradigm'. If permaculture can

[3]KOHN P, McDONALD, G and METCALF, B (1992) 'An Evaluation of Group Titles in Rural Areas' **Queensland Planner**, 32(3), pp 21-26

[4]METCALF, W and VANCLAY, F (1987) *Social Characteristics of Alternative Lifestyle Participants in Australia* IAER, Griffith University: Brisbane

[5]KOHN, P (1991) *Group Title Applicability for Rural Community Living* Unpublished Honours Dissertation, Griffith University

Community Centre which includes dining area, shop and kitchen. Under construction in 1993.

operate as a belief system, ideology or paradigm, then it should help organise the community and ensure the successful operation of Crystal Waters Permaculture Village.

The problem with this is that while everyone who bought a share in Crystal Waters was at least interested in permaculture, and agreed to be bound by a number of legal covenents, there is a great deal of disagreement about what permaculture really means, not in the abstract but in the day-to-day sense.

The situation is complicated by members bringing in other belief systems which they then attach to their own notions of permaculture. For example there is a legal covenant banning the raising of any animals for slaughter, as well as a ban on killing wildlife. Neither of these have anything to do with permaculture, but flow more from the pseudo-Buddhist interests of a number of the community designers and original members. Conflicts have arisen, however, over the fate of chickens at the end of their egg-producing career. Because they were not raised specifically for slaughter, some members argue that they may be killed and eaten. Others argue that the knowledge that chickens could be slaughtered and eaten when no longer productive, simply becomes part of the economics of chicken management, and therefore should be banned under the above rule.

Another issue has arisen around fish. The numerous dams on the property were stocked with fish in an attempt to control mosquitoes (by eating larvae) and to help create natural, aquatic purification systems. Fishing licenses are now being offered and fish hunted and killed in spite of bans on killing wildlife, and raising animals for slaughter, and yet fish must logically fit into one or other of these categories. If fish can be raised for slaughter, then why not pigs? If fish are regarded as wildlife and are then hunted (fished) why ought not the same apply to kangaroos? The arguments have ranged from vitriolic to humourous, but still bylaws are bent and broken, and animals such as fish are being hunted and killed.

A third serious source of conflict has been the covenant on the use of persistent pesticides. State and local government regulations insist that in order to control termites, the area under any concrete slab for a house must be saturated with highly persistent organochlorine pesticides such as chlordane, hep-tachlor, aldrine or dieldrin. Brick, concrete block, mud brick and adobe structures are normally built on a concrete slab, so either these building methods must be abandoned, or the covenant ignored. Several home builders have gone along with government rules and, against the environmental covenants of Crystal Waters, had their blocks sprayed. Crystal Waters Body Corporate (the community), did not punish the offenders, leading to resentment from other members who now find they are living next to where persistent, carcinogenic chemicals have been applied.

> **If fish are regarded as wildlife and are then hunted why ought not the same apply to kangaroos?**

The fourth source of conflict has focused on the operations of the co-operative which was established to facilitate development of community facilities. A proposed 'village centre' was to include a foodshop, post office, craft shop and cafe. It appeared to many members that through poor management, much of the original shareholders' funds which had gone to the co-op had been spent with very little to show in the way of the promised village centre.[6] The meetings around this issue have been acrimonious and inconclusive.

A final source of conflict and contradiction has surrounded the perceived public and educational role of Crystal Waters as a model of good planning and land-use management. As in many intentional communities, there is a perception at Crystal Waters that

they have lessons to share with the rest of the world. The problem is that when people responded to the, at first open, invitation they were seen as intrusive, as tourists, as invading private space, and in some ways as a threat to Crystal Waters. This has lead to various attempts to control visitors by strict signposting at the entrance, to limiting open days to Sundays, by charging for 'tours' and not allowing people to wander about on their own, and by numerous subtle negative messages given to visitors. It is not hard to understand why people have tired of visitors, the same process being observed in communities such as *Findhorn* and the *Centre for Alternative Technology*. But the latter communities recognise visitors as their life-blood, their *raison d'être*, while at Crystal Waters this has yet to be resolved. Intentional community members cannot believe they are a model for the rest of the world while at the same time they resent visitors coming to observe and learn. Obviously there is some middle

[6] *ibid*

ground which members will have to find if they are going remain relevent within the intentional community movement. It would be nice if all visitors had previously read Dave Green and Kat Kinkade's interesting piece on 'How to visit a Community'[7], before visiting Crystal Waters, but such a hope is truly utopian in the worst sense of the term. To regard visitors as, at best a source of revenue and, at worst, as a nuisance, is clearly counterproductive to their stated aims of social change.

Although the path has not been smooth, Crystal Waters is succeeding as an intentional community. So far, in spite of difficulties, it has avoided deteriorating into merely a rural suburb[8]. It has grown to over 100 people, with a reasonably viable economy and excellent housing, within a beautiful natural environment. Many of the original shareholders have sold to newer members, but the community is more stable than most intentional comunities. There is little evidence of a unified concept of permaculture developing, and that may no longer be important to members. The binding force in the community seems to be much more locational and social than ideological. Crystal Waters has used a novel legal structure (Group Titles) and that model has now been taken up by several other intentional communities such as Kookaburra Park, near Bundaberg. Crystal Waters has overcome various crises and will obviously endure and prosper as an intentional community, regardless of permaculture.

[7]GREEN, D and KINKADE, K (1991) 'How to Visit a Community' in COATES, C et al (ed) *Diggers and Dreamers 92/93* Communes Network, some of which is reprinted in the 'Resources' section of this book.

[8]COCK, P (1985) 'Sustaining the Alternative Culture: The Drift Towards Rural Suburbia' *Social Alternatives*, 4(4), pp 12-16

Bill Metcalf is an environmental sociologist at Griffith University, Australia, who has majored in the study of intentional communities throughout the world. His research involvement ranges from Kibbutzim to Survivalists, with group marriages and religious cults in between. For most of his adult life he has lived communally. He is a Fellow of the Findhorn Foundation, Scotland, and has spent one to two months there every year since 1988. He is one of the original shareholders in Crystal Waters Permaculture Village, but continues to live (mainly) in Brisbane.

CRYSTAL WATERS
PERMACULTURE VILLAGE
PRIVATE ROAD
PLEASE DRIVE SLOWLY **40**
PEDESTRIANS, CYCLISTS AND ANIMALS HAVE RIGHT OF WAY AT ALL TIMES ON ALL ROADS
PLEASE NOTE THAT DOGS AND CATS ARE NOT PERMITTED

Currie being fired for going on television with a few unpalatable truths about the effects of factory farming and causing severe tremors in the market for Chicken Futures before being dragged off camera with a hook.

Shortly thereafter, four rather handsome reddish-brown hens joined the communal family, as some of us like to think of it; though others were thinking rather more of sage-and-onion stuffing at Gas Mark 5.

If you have hens, and if you also happen to have foxes - and we have foxes like some people have field mice because the local Hunt is forbidden to cross our land and foxes aren't stupid - then the first critical requirement is a good strong henhouse.

Joan proceeded to advertise for one in the local paper and was amazed to discover that the countryside was full of people with surplus henhouses to unload. Indeed, so eager were these people to be helpful that several of them drove their henhouses up here on lorries and unloaded them on our forecourt on a "trial

basis".

Suddenly, the front of The Lodge looked like Chicken Tent City or possibly Trump Towers, and the hens, each of whom now had a desirable detached residence of her own, were looking at each other like the ballplayers in Field of Dreams: "Is this heaven? No, it's Borsetshire!"

Soon, the hens were laying, and all might have been well had it not been for Pam's Auntie Freda. Auntie Freda runs a sort of farm-cum-tourist hostel down in Dorset that makes Cold Comfort Farm look like The Design Centre, and she happened to have some surplus baby chicks. "You have hens," she said to Pam. "Why not have more? Have another seven!"

Well, time passed and the seven chicks grew up and three of them were cockerels. And of course you never keep your own cockerels (Immutable Law of the Countryside Number 6,732), so off they went to market for a handsome return (24p per bird), and the woman who had sold Joan the original four hens then sold us a cockerel.

"So good for the eggs, dear - makes them more nutritious! And the chickens do enjoy it, you know!"

This was how Snuffy came into our lives. Snuffy, when he arrived, was a miserable, downtrodden creature, clearly the runt of his litter and an obvious victim of preordained Darwinian pecking, not to say assault with a deadly weapon. But nothing puts

Drawing by Catriona Stamp

Cometh the Day, Cometh the Chicken

*S*ometimes we have to remind ourselves that our community at The Lodge is privileged to be set in some of the most idyllic countryside England can offer. Hills to the right of us, hills to the left of us; flowers, trees, squirrels and mud all around us.

And all there for the taking by the simple act of looking out the window or opening the front door - acts that many of us rarely perform ("Put another log on the fire, Bill old chap, and pass The Times, would you? Thanks very much!").

But this air of superior urban detachment is a little harder to maintain when the primal forces of nature stop sitting around looking like an Ecover detergent advert and instead rise up in their wrath to smite you. Even as I write, those same primal forces are strutting purposefully up and down outside our hastily erected barricades and The Lodge has come to resemble the Los Angeles police outpost in John Carpenter's Assault on Precinct 13.

We're thinking of sending Christabel, the seven-year-old, on a desperate dash down the road to get reinforcements, but we're not at all sure she'd make it and if the worst happened her parents might be annoyed. And then one of the adults might have to brave the forces of evil out there in her stead.

Bill and Ann, who help run the local Film Society, have suggesting faxing Ridley Scott to come and record the unfolding horror

on film, but Jake pointed out that we have very large windows here which admit far too much light for a Ridley Scott production. And anyway, by the time the crew finished lunch at The Dorchester and got down here from London, none of us might be left to draw the storyboard.

But speaking of storyboards, it's probably best to begin at the beginning.

The beginning was around the time that Joan, Humanistic Psychotherapist and Mother of Two, altered her work schedule to spend more time at home. It wasn't long afterwards that she began to feel a strange desire to re-establish contact with the basic forces of Gaia. Women, as is well known, feel these forces more keenly than men. And in Joan's subconscious, and in her faithfully recorded dreams, Gaia was coming increasingly to resemble a chicken.

"I know how we all feel about pets," said Joan at a Sunday night meeting, "but if no one objects, I'm thinking of getting some hens - for the eggs, you know. Think of the money we'll save! And, we'll be absolutely sure that every egg we eat is free-range. Moral certainty is so important in these troubled times, don't you think?"

None of us gave a toss for moral certainty, and we didn't even care all that much about the money. But the argument that really broke our resistance was over Salmonella, since many of us remembered the fearless and public-spirited ex-Minister Edwina

hair on the chest of the persecuted faster than being shifted from the bottom of one pecking order to the top of another. Ask the late Austrian ex-house painter! Ask Snuffy!

Within weeks, Snuffy had sorted out the hens, organising them into an efficient and well-drilled Garden Deconstruction Brigade visiting each part of the estate in a kind of cropping rotation that took in flowers and vegetables indiscriminately and without prejudice.

It was only then that Snuffy turned his attention to the self-styled Lords of the Manor. The first victim, by a cruel twist of fate, was the Arch-Vegetarian Pete, innocently bearing a bucket out to the compost bin on a fine, bright afternoon. Behind the bin, lurking in ambush, was the demented Chicken - and as Pete turned to go back to the house, Snuffy attacked in a swirl of claws and beak. As Pete later recounted the story, it was only a savage boot to the head, putting Snuffy down for a long eight-count, that allowed the shaken purveyor of lentils to escape.

Joan, whose attempts to look sympathetic reminded some of us of Ian Holm's company android in Alien, then placed a black and vicious-looking stick by the front door. "You'll be all right out there if you wave that stick around," she told us. "Remember - the only thing we have to fear is fear itself!"

That pious hope was laid to rest - as indeed Ann almost was - when Snuffy chased her a full fifty yards across the forecourt, slashing away at stick as well as

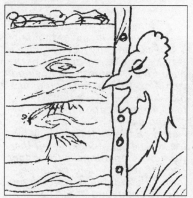

Drawing by Catriona Stamp

legs, and then tried to force his way into the front hall after her. "I don't care how fresh the eggs are," wailed Ann, who never knowingly kills even so much as a fly (she catches them in tumblers and escorts them out of the room). "I'm not going out there again! It's him or us! And it better be Coq au Vin!"

At the moment, however, that seems unlikely. Night is falling and crowing sounds are coming ever nearer our makeshift lines of cement bags and overstuffed cushions. There are strange scrabbling noises in the cellar. Joan seems remarkably unconcerned, but some of the rest of us are busy rewriting our wills ...

Bob Fromer is an American who has been marooned in Britain since 1969 and who has lived communally since 1972, first in London, then at Blue Frog House in Kington, Herefordshire and, since 1984, at Birchwood Hall. He's still trying to decide whether intentional communities are a model for future generations or a middle class indulgence - or both. During the late 1980s Bob wrote a series of columns for The Guardian about a fictional community called The Lodge. 'Cometh the Day' and 'Like Thieves in the Night' (page 72) continue the series.

A Commune that works ... so far

KAT KINKADE

I suppose one really never knows if it's safe to go public with a statement that a commune "works". There will always be a cautious voice to say that it's too early to tell. After all Oneida Community lasted nearl 40 years before it's demise. Twin Oaks where I live is merely 26 years old, so I may be premature in boasting that it works.. But I'm going to take the risk. At worst, I will some-day look back on this article with a wry face. At best, I can share some of what we've learned and provide some signposts at the crossroads of decision-making. We are probably not going to be the last people ever to try communal living.

At Twin Oaks, after a quarter of a century, we can take a thoughtful look over the road we've come. Not all the evidence is in, but by most standards we're a modest success. Never in those years has any member lacked food or medical care. Our housing and clothing standards don't satisfy us yet, but they're improving. We've grown from 8 to 80+ people: we have built ten major buildings, including a central kitchen and dining room. Our kids lack nothing and in most cases better educated than they would have been in separate families. Our social security is total, cradle to grave. We take care of each other in the pro-foundest sense. Our lives are busy , active and inter-esting. And we have managed to keep our door open to new members who meet minimal standards of compatability and willingness to work, all this with a common treasury and no private capitalism to speak of. No guru either. Our leaders, when we have had any, have been the ordinary political variety you could follow if you chose, and if not, you could oppose, depose or ignore.

Twin Oaks in the USA always seems like the community that's got it all sorted out. This article was originally written seven years ago but we've decided to reprint it because - as an analysis of the factors that ensure sustainablility - it is completely timeless.

So maybe it isn't out of place to assume we're making it and to speculate on the reasons. I think there are maybe 20 big decisions every commune has to make, and if you get a right answer to about twelve of them you win. You can afford to be wrong on the other eight, because there isn't one right recipe, and even the definitions of success are pleasantly flexible. Take, for example, the matter of getting the work done. Our watchword was "equality", and we went to enormous lengths to be sure that all our work was distributed as evenly as possible. We've had a lot of theoretical discussions over the years on such matters as whether the untrained have as much right as the skilled to a given task, and whether we should assure a 50/50 assignment of the sexes to various crews. I don't give this stuff much credit for our survival; it's just one of the fascinating aspects of our particular culture. What is vital is that the work gets done and that those who shouldered a lot of responsibility didn't feel so ripped off that they left with no one to take their places. I know other successful groups that have answered the work question in ways quite different from ours. What we share with those groups is that we make sure the work gets done and that we feel okay about its distribution.

Okay, that was number one. Getting the work done without feeling ripped off. There are a bunch of others. For instance, we keep enough money coming in. This is easier said than done if you're rural. We had, and still have, no business geniuses among us, and we're still not rich. What we have learned and practice is this: find something that looks like it might work, go at it with diligence, take some risks, *put about half your total work force on it*, and you're likely to be able to make a living. That's a grim picture for two reasons. One is that the other half of the work force probably has babies to take care of, and the other is that it is sales, not production, that requires the initial efforts in most businesses, and selling ability isn't common among us. Twin Oaks' day-to-day labour demands aren't too bad these days, because we have fewer than 20 children, so the people who aren't bringing in money can be doing the other necessary tasks. At this point, we can afford to keep only a third of our labour force in money-making activities. I don't by any means think Twin Oaks is a model to follow for income production. We did the best we could, and we are economically secure enough, but there are probably better ways for other groups. What we did right, though, was to resist the impulse to try to live off the land and faced the necessity of making money in the nation's marketplace. Another feasible way is to work at jobs in cities (we did that for a few years as a stopgap, and we sure don't recommend it if there's an alternative). One way or another the group has to have enough cash to provide the kinds of things that its members consider essential.

We maintain a communal economy. The essence of the benefit of pooled resourses is that once you have spent what you need to for the basic maintenance of the group, what you have left over is a big enough lump of money to do something with. If you divide up the money and distribute it each worker's ambitions are limited by the small amount of resources. In such an economy there are lots of tape-players and bicycles. But in a communal economy, the "surplus" is big enough for something that serves the community. Such a community has sidewalks and sewage works. Eventually it gets tape-players and bicycles too.

We held the line on consumption. Twin Oaks' early leaders were very stingy with consumer goodies. Most of the surplus cash, when we had any, went into buildings, tools and business investment. That same conservatism, though loosening somewhat in recent years, is still basic to our financial thinking. If we didn't put large chunks of the surplus into permanent investment the lack of facilities would discourage serious communards from choosing our way of life.

We keep the door open. The lifeline of Twin Oaks is its visitor program. One major way that we have not succeeded is that we have not figured out a way to keep the same people here for their whole lives. Some stay only a few months, a third of us have five to ten communal years behind us. We console ourselves by saying this is somewhat longer than the national average for our age group. We feel saddened by this nonetheless, and we keep trying to find ways to "cut turnover" as we put it.

The lifeline of Twin Oaks is its visitor program

We don't accept badly screwed-up people. We have learned that we cannot cure emotionally disturbed people, and we send them away. This was a tough decision to make, but it was the right decision. Experience quickly showed us that forcing ourselves to live with people who made us uncomfortable cost us far, far more than any good we might have done for them. We no longer have any notion of ourselves as a therapeutic community. This certainly doesn't mean that a therepeutic community couldn't work - for people who choose to do just that.

We leave people's minds alone. In spite of the standard liberal beliefs implicit in our policies and customs, we really do not insist on intellectual or spiritual conformity. We are based on ideals of equality but have members in good standing who think equality is nonsense and say so. What we do instead is base our policy making on some reasonable but compromised version of the equality idea and try to get people to go along with it. We are as a group, non-sexist, non-racist,no-nageist, non-competative and so on. As individuals we vary a whole lot on all of it. We also vary on the degree to which we think we ought to be striving towards our ideals. In fact there is almost nothing we don't have a variety of opinions on. When this becomes clear to outsiders or new people, they ask with bewilderment, "But then how do you come to agreement?". The answer is that we don't. We manage pretty well without it. What we have instead is widely delegated control of some of the basics, a substantial body of useful tradition, a general habit of most of us going by most of the rules most of the time, and a lot of giving in to each other on small matters in order to make our whole community effort work. We compromise on everything. I'm not sure why I think this is a survival technique, but I sense that it is. Maybe it's because members who can't compromise generally leave us for what they call ideological reasons. We tend to attract, select and create tolerant people. Compromise hasn't always been a Twin Oaks watchword. In the early years, we tried to stand true to various principles. But if we had been rigid about it, we would have lost too many members at once, and the community would have died young. In order to keep on going we made hybrid policies based on whatever the current members would accept (including what our ideals could stomach), and somewhere along the line we stopped being ashamed of it and started boasting about it.

> We compromise on everything. I'm not sure why I think this is a survival technique, but I sense that it is.

We have systems. Twin Oaks is unabashedly organised. There is an irony in this, because we may be some of the freest people on earth. We didn't set out to create such a complex organization. It was no part of our initial idealism to have a massive underbrush of committees, crews, teams, councils, mangagers and what not to keep our communal lives in order. We just created them as we saw the need and there they are. Do I claim that this bureaucracy is a survival characteristic? In a sense I do. I claim that it is a safe alternative to strong leadership. What is wrong with strong leadership? For one thing able leaders are not very common. But a bigger problem is the likelihood that their inspirations may be wrong. Our cheerful acceptance of the neccessity of organisation allows us to be a big community.

Which leads to another survival characteristic: size. Small groups have to be very lucky to survive if they have any significant membership turnover. I have heard of small groups without turnover but it's not the norm. Bigger is safer. Twin Oaks went from its original eight members up to our present 80-plus just as fast as conditions would allow. During several years of treading water while the national media lost interest in us, our sheer bulk kept us from going under. It would be hard to kill Twin Oaks: there's too much of it. We've got those by-laws which prevent anyone making a profit from dissolution, for one thing; and all those die-hards who refuse to give in when things get discouraging: and then there are the people who come with fresh enthusiasm. If Twin Oaks lost 30 people tomorrow, we would be very, very upset, if we got hit with some kind of bill for half a million dollars, we would be very discouraged, but we would not cease to exist. We would just adjust and keep going. We have no guru to tell us when it is all over, and a very low probability on agreeing to dissolve. I suppose we might compromise, but that would leave us a remnant that would rebuild Twin Oaks. We change. We never allow Twin Oaks to stagnate for very long. If we have money, we frequently build a needed building; if we don't, we work on something else, like improvements in our culture or government or business or interpersonal relationships. Usually we move ahead on both material and social fronts at the same time. Is this necessary for survival? Certainly it keeps some of us from being bored. It provides a feeling of being part of something vital, something to which each member can have input.

At this point the line grows fuzzy. How much else of what we are is necessary for our survival, and how much is just a loving description of Twin Oaks? We don't really know. Will we make it? We don't know that either, but it looks like it to me. True, 26 years isn't long and we aren't very big or very important. Just the same, Twin Oaks really is fully communal, and it really does work. I'd give it another 50 years easy.

Kat Kinkade is one of the founding members (1967) of Twin Oaks commune in Louisa ,Virginia, USA She spent nine years there, and another five at East Wind, Twin Oaks' sister commune in Missouri She has written a book about the early days at Twin Oaks and is currently working on another book about Twin Oaks. She now lives back at Twin Oaks.

Communities in early 20th Century Britain

Legend:
- ◆ Religious Anarchist community
- ❖ Anarchist Communist community
- ✾ Garden City influenced community
- ᚷ Eric Gill inspired community
- ⚑ Land Settlement Association site
- ✺ World War II Pacifist community
- ▒ Area with extensive Plotlands developments

Stirling Homesteads ✾

Stannington ⚑
⚑ Broadwath
⚑ Crofton
⚑ Dalston
❖ Clousden Hill, Newcastle

◆ Brotherhood Church, Pontefract
⚑ Snaith

⚑ Oxcroft
✺ Holton Beckering
⚑ Harrowby
⚑ Fulney

⚑ Elmesthorpe

Capel-y-Ffin, ᚷ
nr Abergavenny

✺ Gloucester Land Scheme
◆ Whiteway Colony

⚑ Newent

Pigotts, ᚷ
nr High Wycombe

⚑ Chawston   ⚑ Fen Drayton
⚑ Potton   ⚑ Abington ✺ Elmset, Ipswich
              ⚑ Denham
              ⚑ Newbourn

Kingston Comm Farm ✺
Charney Basset
⚑ Andover

Yeldham ⚑⚑
& Foxash
✺ Moore Place, Stanford-le-Hope

ᚷ Hopkins Crank, Ditchling
⚑ Sidlesham

❖ Marsh House
❖ Fellowship House
✾ Brentham Estate
London

Intentional Communities in the first half of the Twentieth Century: Overview

"There is no doubt that we are on the verge of a new era in civilisation. With regard to war, love, birth, death, morals and art, we all know that some thoughts and actions are doomed and that others are ready to take their place."

Edith Lees, a Member of Fellowship House, 1921

A t a first glance the early part of this century seems sparsely populated by communal ventures. The great wave of nineteenth century utopianism had all but died out and the 'new wave' communities of the 1960s and 70s were still over the horizon. But when one delves a little deeper into the largely unwritten history of ordinary people of the times, through local history society publications, magazines from the period and oral histories, a picture starts to build up of a widespread patchwork of communal and co-operative activities going on.

We have tried in this section to cover the various strands of the 'movement' during this period, many of which can be traced back into the previous century (see 'Communalism in the Nineteenth Century' in *Diggers and Dreamers 92/93*). Some communities, like The Brotherhood Church can trace their roots back to the late 1800s. A major strand of communalism throughout the period grew out of the Utopian Socialist ideas that had inspired nineteenth century communards. The ideas of people like William Morris and Peter Kropotkin were, in the early twentieth century, to filter out to a much wider number of people in some fairly large-scale movements. These various movements: the Garden Cities movement; the Plotlands movement; the Arts and Crafts movement; and the Land Settlement Association were all not only a somewhat romantic 'back to the

The popular myth is that communes were invented during the sixties. In previous editions of *Diggers and Dreamers* we've described communes of earlier centuries. This time we hope that we can scotch the myth once and for all by presenting information on communities which existed in Britain between 1900 and 1945

land' reaction to industrialisation, but also part of a pre-welfare state provision of a better life. They were sometimes encouraged by a degree of official government backing. These experiments, some more communal in character than others are covered in the article by Colin Ward: 'Colonising the Land'; and the pieces on the communities at Brentham and Stirling. Outside of these more mainstream movements various religious communities such as The Bruderhof (see entry 23 in the Directory section) continued to flourish. Other communities were inspired by charismatic individuals like Eric Gill the sculptor. The Second World War caused a number of pacifists to turn to communal living not just as a means of avoiding conscription but as a way towards a more peaceful world. These communities are detailed by Andrew Rigby in 'Pacifist Islands in a Martial Sea'. After the War the emerging state welfare provision took away much of the impetus from, and need for, the various co-operative and communal 'welfare' schemes. This led ultimately to a watering down of the original ideals and aspirations of the schemes' instigators and participants.

Wherever land was cheap car owning city-dwellers would buy plots of land and often build their own dwellings. At "plotlands" developments like Jaywick Sands in Essex (shown above) a real sense of community was often created - although not always intentionally.

COME TO PEACEHAVEN!

The Brotherhood Church: A century of communal living.

CHRIS COATES

A self-published book *The History of the Brotherhood Church* by Alfred Higgins chronicles the lives and times of what turns out to be a fascinating link between various strands of the co-operative/communities movement covering the last century.

Initially a revolutionary Christian anarchist network of groups inspired in part by both the writings of Tolstoy and a young Irish minister called J Bruce Wallace, who in 1887 published a weekly journal called *Brotherhood*. By 1895 an active network had been established in Croydon.

"They printed their own paper, established a shop where various goods were sold at cost price, did dressmaking, made hosiery and had plans for a laundry."

The following year they were involved in setting up a colony on 10 acres at Purleigh in Essex. Also involved were W Sinclair, S Protheroe and Nellie Shaw who were all later pioneers at the Whiteway Anarchist Colony in Gloucestershire (see 'Whiteway: The Anarchist Arcadia' in *D&D 92/93*).

Following an engineering strike in Leeds in 1897 a local electrician and cycle maker turned his workshop over to a workers' collective. A group of men lived and worked at the workshop and it became a meeting place for The Brotherhood Church. One member, D B Foster wrote in his life story that:

"The history of this experiment in communistic activity is not easy for me to write, as to me it is a story of infinite joy and inexpressable disappointments ... I learned more in those two or three years than I had learned in the past

Communities may come and Communities may go but the Brotherhood Church goes on forever it seems

*twenty ... Throughout the week, work and discussion were
interwoven, and on Sundays the time was devoted to worship, prayer and education."*

Foster was a business man and he soon perceived
that where people are 'free' to work or talk, too much
time is apt to be spent on talk, however uplifting the
talk may be. When he suggested regular work hours,
it did not appeal to all the idealists and this lead to
the gradual break up of the group. A few members
went on to join a group in Blackburn which operated
an electrical business partly on a no-money basis (an
early LETS scheme?). By 1903/4 the Blackburn and
the Purleigh groups had folded. From about this time
'til 1920/21 the 'church' again existed as a network
with a base in Beeston, Leeds. Keeping up links with
the Whiteway Colony and others and being involved
with pacifist opposition to the 1914-18 War and helping conscientious objectors.

*In 1921 a small group moved to a smallholding at
Stapleton, near Pontefract and although rumoured
to have folded they are still very much in exsistence.
There follows an interview with Hilda and Len
Gibson (residents at the community) and Peter
(Hilda's brother) and his wife.*

Hilda The main thing the Brotherhood Church has
stood for really, it's been a Christian group, and when
we say Christian we mean taking the sermon on the
mount seriously. Not particularly bothering with the
Old Testament. I mean it's alright knowing what's in
it, taking the teaching of Jesus Christ seriously and
doing their utmost to align our lives as a group and as
individuals on that basis. And you could say whilst
we don't make an issue of breaking laws, if we feel
the laws of the land conflict with the teachings of
Jesus Christ then we quite readily ignore the laws of
the land ... in 1921 when they moved out here some
of the people remained at the community house in
Beeston. Our parents moved here in 1926. First they
had the community house, then this house was built
behind, when our parents came out they built a
house where that one is now, just beyond the lilac.
This had been a bare field in 1921, a field of turnips.
Far more open than it is now ... it was bought from
the Stapleton Park estate and there were complica-
tions in regard to the buying. Two or three of the men
in Leeds had gone around the country looking at various pieces of land and this estate was up for auc-
tion at the end of 1920. We have a series of letters in
the deed box from Lilian Ferris, because she had had

....
**if we feel the
laws of the
land conflict
with the
teachings of
Jesus Christ
then we quite
readily ignore
the laws of the
land**
....

some money left and that's why she was writing, her money was going to pay for the land. £250 for 7 acres. The deal all worked out and she said, "Well there is just one more thing, we don't really go along with title deeds. So this made quite a complication. The Brotherhood weren't prepared to have anything to do with the title deeds so we had a receipt for the money. What we've always said is that everything that's done on this piece of land is not really done for personal gain, or engrandisement, but for the sake of building the church and the ideas for which we stand ...

Throughout its history the Brotherhood Church had always held a deep felt anti-authoritarian position; conducting its own marriage ceremonies, refusing to fill in census returns; conscientious objection. At Stapleton this brought them into a series of conflicts with the local authorities. Through refusing to register the births of children; home educating their children; refusal to pay land tithes; refusing both ration card and identity cards; and the erection of houses without planning permission. In the last instance the houses were knocked down by the authority and promptly rebuilt by the community.

Chris How do you get on with the authorities now?

Hilda We got on with them OK until they brought in the poll tax. We call things on this land part of the Brotherhood Church. Now we don't really go in for voting 'cause they don't represent us anyway. A lot of people take that attitude without making an issue of it. For many years Alf Higgins was the only one here who got a voting card because he wrote to them and told them he wasn't going to vote for their lousy system. After a period Len thought well it's time he wrote to them and tell them he wasn't going to take part in their lousy voting system so they gave him a vote. I haven't yet written to tell them so I don't get one ... when they send the voting card they address it to Church of the Brotherhood, from the very same council office where the poll tax people write to us addressing us as The Bungalow, New Road, Stapleton. In fact they sent us two demands for my father who had died. Now we didn't think it was right to pay twice for a house that wasn't occupied. I have a sheaf of letters ... in the end I said to them: "Are you a computer or are you a human being like me, you know you don't answer anything I say, you just keep on sending these things back and back and back again" ... In the end a woman phoned us and I said we'll come and have a chat with you, and as it was getting on towards the end of July I thought it would be a good idea if we had this meeting on Hiroshima Day. So I suggested this to Len ... and we went along and saw her in her cubicle like you might visit a person in prison, with this screen in between you, really it was a horrible place. We told her our point of view. They had exemptions for religious communities. She kept on about the nuns and monks at Hazelwood Castle, they registered first and then applied for exemption afterwards. We said well we don't do it that way. We gave them some very good reasons why the authorities had already regarded us as a religious community ...

Len We brought up the thing about the address. Also when our eldest boy had first started work and was unemployed and needed to claim social security they wouldn't give it to him because they said he was a member of a religious community ...

Chris So did you pay?

Len No, we just kept sending the letters back "not known at this address ... "

Hilda Over the years going back, my father was trained as a teacher just before the First World War, and he taught in schools for a very short time. He decided he didn't like the way things were done in ordinary schools and he gave up teaching ... one of our chief leaflet writers Tom Ferris (they used to write leaflets directed at certain bodies of people) he wrote a leaflet that was addressed to the Teacher Training College in Leeds. This was how my father, Alf Higgins, heard of the Brotherhood Church. The people in the Brotherhood chose to educate their own children. We didn't go to school. My brother never went to school, I went to a free school when I was 13. Most of the children here were educated at home, without being examined by anybody. We must confess when we had our children, there were no other children here. Our eldest son was 5 when we had twins and he was longing to go to school. So we conceded and let him go to the local school and the twins later, I think they wanted the company ... I wasn't sure about that. I know that there was somebody else that was brought up in this house, she didn't go to school and she felt she had been lonely in her childhood. So she was thankful when our children went to school, but I felt a bit too guilty ...

Chris What sort of reaction do you get from the local churches? Do they regard you as another church?

Len (Laughs) No. We know some of the ministers. We meet on friendly terms.

Hilda They do know that we stand for different things. We repair their vehicles for them. We do printing for them. They know that we will do a fair job. We believe if we do a job for anyone in doing a fair job whatever it is ...

Chris Do you have a communal purse?

Hilda Well at one time everyone did and then people felt the importance of the family unit was greater. We share implements and tackle but we live as family units. That was decided way back in the 1930s.

Len People contribute what they can if there is any repairs or whatever ...

Chris You said your father kept bees and you, Len, were a mechanic, what did other people do

Hilda Before they moved to the country there was the knitting industry that we had. Making knitted goods, socks, jerseys, all sorts of knitted goods. We still have sock machines. This was one of our main industries throughout the First World War 'til everyone moved from Leeds. In fact the hexagonal building was built with windows on all sides for use as a knitting room. and that was one of the quite extensive sources of income right up until clothes were rationed in the Second World War ...

Peter There was some people in the Leeds community did some work on early fridges ...

Len What did Charles Stimson do?

Peter When he was here he worked the land. Sidney Overbury kept goats, and he did have two or three hives and he would go and do work for local farmers, he did threshing with them ... he would sell produce, kept some hens ...

Hilda My mother ran a green house - not the one there now- she grew tomatoes and things. There was a lot of rhubarb grown here, that my father used to take into Castleford and his mother would sell it to everyone down the street ... We do all sorts of things. I mean Len's now doing printing. Actually some of the Tramp Preachers, the Brotherhood of the way[1], they did printing here for a time ... and peace campaigning as well. Last but not least by any manner of means ... in a way the work Len did with the film van going all over the country for approximately a quarter of each year.

Len I did that from 1960 until 1988, 27 years. I used to do it for the Peace Pledge Union, although it started from here. I really did the same sort of thing as what the Tramp Preachers did. It was a rear projection, you lifted the back and there was the screen and I showed the film from the inside ... all anti-war films, mostly shorts because your audience was a passing audience.

Hilda To begin with it went out from here with local support from local friends, then some of the PPU thought it was such a good idea that they bought the van so Len could run it for much longer periods. It was our baby, but it became a message from the Peace

[1] The Brotherhood of the way, or tramp preachers were a group of itinerant preachers who had connections with the Brotherhood Church in the early days (1920s - 50s)

Pledge Union and the War Resisters International.

Len I went pretty well all over England, Wales. I spent a month in Ireland at the time of the troubles ... One of the reasons for coming out onto the land was because it was felt we hadn't just to think about treating human beings right, you had to treat all things that were part of mother earth, not just the animals and the humans but also the ground. This ground has been

totally organic since we came here in 1921. There has been no artifical fertilisers, pesticides or pollutants or whatever used on the land. Up 'til very recently we were using a well that was sunk by striking mine blasters and some of our own labour for drinking water, and our washing water was collected from rainwater in underground tanks ...

Chris Do you have any legal structure?

Hilda There's trustees, but not in the sense of a legal trust. There are nine people ... in the very early days it was assumed that the male head of the family was a trustee, going back to a different set of ideas in a different time - even though they supported the suffer-agettes ... when we didn't pay rates in the early days it was the male heads of families that were the ones that went to prison, because they took the position of being trustees. Later things rode on, after some of those people died, without trustees in a certain sense. Then when we were having some more hassle with somebody who was later asked to leave we felt it was essential to reappoint trustees ... so we extended our trustee numbers to nine about two years ago, so we have nine trustees, people that care ...

· · · · · · · · · · · · · · · · · · · ·

This ground has been totally organic since we came here in 1921

· · · · · · · · · · · · · · · · · · · ·

The history which precedes this interview is gleaned from the following sources:

HIGGINS AG (1982) *A History of the Brotherhood Church* The Brotherhood Church, Stapleton, near Pontefract, Yorkshire.

QUAIL, J (1978) *The Slow Burning Fuse* Paladin, London

Also available from The Brotherhood Church:

GIBSON, H *Much Requested Vegetarian Recipes* (2nd ed 1992)

Annual Brotherhood Calender

STIMSON, Rev C *The Price To Be Paid "The Tramp Preachers"* (1988)

Chris Coates is a member of People in Common. He has lived in community for 14 years.

Chris They're not all residents?

Hilda No. Len and I are classed as resident trustees, my brother and his wife are also trustees and there's five other trustees including my daughter ... There's a couple living in that house who are not fully fledged members, they class themselves as visitors and so do we, though the mother of the young man down there was born into the Brotherhood ...

Chris Do you think any of your children will come back & live here ?

Hilda I think it's highly likely, they seem to do such a lot here ... you see our sons don't admit to necessarily going along with all the things we do, but especially the oldest one he says that he is determined to ensure that this place goes on with the same ideas that it started with. He admits that he doesn't live his life that way ... They've been involved with hunt-sabbing and fighting the poll tax because it was evil ... When we have a meeting for worship, or for a special occasion, we have a meeting a bit like the Quaker meeting ... we do sometimes say well we're nearer to Quakers than other things, but we're more like the early Quakers than the present day ones.

Chris In what way ?

Hilda ... you see the original Friends took the teachings of the sermon on the mount, things like that seriously, and disregarded the state if it was interfering with their beliefs. Now a lot of the Friends don't do that and they're much more middle-class than they were in the early days. Those are the sort of things I mean. There are a lot of good Friends, I'm not wishing to put the modern Friends down. But I think probably in the 1600s people were rebelling against the way things were at that time and you might say we continue to rebel against the way things are ...

Chris What's the secret of keeping going for a hundred years?

Len (Laughs) Faith.

Hilda A bit of new blood now and again ... and sticking to the principles that are eternal.

Sex, Politics and Housework

JUDY GREENWAY

By the end of the Nineteenth Century, most English anarchists were committed to the idea of equality but the trouble was that men's and women's ideas of what this meant often differed, and even where there was agreement in principle, the practice was something else. The numerous anarchist experiments in communitarian living which flourished from the 1890s onwards brought out some of the difficulties and contradictions in attempting to change what it meant to be a man or a woman. Sexual relationships and housework were particular sources of tension.

Women often took a leading role in setting up anarchist communities. What did they hope to gain? In 1912, Lily Gair Wilkinson wrote:

"I believe that if we begin with immediate personal things, greater and greater opportunities are likely to occur ... I wish to express anarchism in my life."

She saw daily life as one form of political propaganda, and may well have been thinking of her young anarchist friends living communally in Marsh House in London.

Two decades earlier, another communal London household, Fellowship House, promised its inhabitants all the advantages and obligations of a family without any of its drawbacks, according to member Edith Lees. She argued that women should reject servitude in the home as she and her comrades did.

Men also deliberated over the role of women in such communities. In 1894 Henry Binns advertised for other people to help start a fruit-growing co-

"The men sit and philosophise while the women get on with the work" was a comment made in the 1930s by a woman living at Whiteway - the anarchist rural colony, founded (in 1898) on the principle of equality of the sexes!

operative, but he was worried because it "... bids fair to become a Bachelor's Club," or else a group of married couples and single men. He wanted:

> "An open, honourable, honest fellowship such as we dream of and talk of ... but for the most part fail to make for ourselves ... But, frankly, can we trust ourselves to live above suspicions ... and jealousies? And, frankly, are our women comrades fitted and ready for useful work? ... We want women to help us; we cannot succeed without them; women who want to work for their own living ... who are as eager to be truer women as we are to be truer men."

In 1897, journalist Henry Nevinson recorded in his diary a visit to Clousden Hill anarchist colony near Newcastle. After naming and describing some of the men, he wrote:

> "Kapper showed me round ... The leeks, cabbages, rhubarb, celery, strawberries, roses, pansies were good ... Mushrooms were supposed to be growing in the glasshouse ... About 100 chickens, 20 ducks, 3 cows, 6 goats. Some rabbits, 2 horses, and a dog were the livestock: also one woman and three children."

... About 100 chickens, 20 ducks, 3 cows, 6 goats. Some rabbits, 2 horses, and a dog were the livestock: also one woman and three children.

This anonymity and relegation of women is a recurrent feature of many records. To what extent it reflects the status of women rather than the attitudes of the (male) recorder is difficult to tell. In any case, women were frequently in a minority in the early days. Single women joining mixed communities ran the risk of social and familial disapproval and rejection. Edith Lees believed one reason why so few women were involved in the Fellowship of the New Life was that women thought that ideals of sex and class equality, moral regeneration and the simple life were all very well, but impractical.

Once they had joined a community, women often found housework was a major problem. Peter Kropotkin, whose writings influenced many early living experiments, advised the founders of Clousden Hill to:

> "do all possible for reducing household work to the lowest minimum ... Arrangements to reduce as much as possible the incredible amount of work which women uselessly spend in the rearing up of children, as well as in the household work, are ... as essential to the success of the community as the proper arrangement of the fields, the greenhouses, and the agricultural machinery. Even more"

The anarchist feminist journal *The Freewoman* carried regular debate on the housework question in 1911/12. One contributor wrote:

> *"As a convinced feminist and aspiring freewoman, I feel that this question of housework ... is absolutely fundamental ... Women have no time to get free. They will only have the time when domestic work has been properly organised."*

Solutions offered ranged from machine age fantasies to schemes for collective and co-operative living. The professionalisation of domestic work was another alternative, though women who already earned their living as servants weren't convinced that life would be much better working for a collective household than for individual employers. The simple life held the promise of less housework anyway - but what did this mean in practice?

The Clousden Hill Prospectus says that all housework is:

> *"... to be done on the most improved system, to relieve the women from the long and tiresome work which unduly falls to their share today ..."*

What this meant in real life is not recorded, though in 1897 a visitor noted that men did the washing, women the cooking and mending.

Whiteway began on communistic lines, and the women did the domestic work including washing, mending and cooking for all the men. Eventually the colony moved away from communalism - amongst other reasons, the women rebelled against doing all the washing when some of the men wouldn't even collect firewood to heat the water. The women preferred to do housework for just one man rather than for all of them.

Other early communities varied in whether men were expected to do housework. Henry Binns wrote

the women rebelled against doing all the washing when some of the men wouldn't even collect firewood to heat the water

Edith Lees, an enthusiastic member of The Fellowship of the New Life. A collection of her essays - The New Horizon in Love and Life - was published after her death in her married name, Mrs Havelock Ellis.

that in his proposed colony, women would do:

"Not 'housework' only... but joining us in our work as far as they will and can, and we so far, joining in theirs."

In Marsh House, before and during World War One, both sexes shared the housework, but when Tom Keell, the editor of the anarchist paper *Freedom*, moved in, he was exempted because his own work was more important - a recurring theme in male/female relationships.

Even when the women didn't feel that housework was more natural to them, they often ended up doing it on the grounds of efficiency, because men did it so much more incompetently. Men in men-only collectives would do their own, though some middle class men felt humiliated to be seen doing "women's and servants' work" such as scrubbing steps. In Edward Carpenter's homosexual household at Millthorpe, though women visitors spoke admiringly of his domestic skills, they noted that his working class lover took on the major responsibility for running the house. In mixed communities, working class women were more likely than the other women to end up doing most of the work.

Often, women did both "women's" and "men's" work, as at Whiteway where they were involved in agriculture and building. On their own, co-operatively, or as part of a family business, some would earn money by traditional female occupations such as dressmaking, weaving or craftwork. This was sometimes the major or only source of family income while the men got on with what was seen as the more important political work.

In mixed communities, working class women were more likely than the other women to end up doing most of the work.

Two patterns repeat themselves: one is of women's own political and economic contribution being undervalued - both by themselves and historians. (We hear about the men who produced the newspapers - what about the women who provided the food so they could do it?) The other is of women who were doing the domestic chores, raising children, earning money, and also participating in collective work. It is not surprising that few women had the time to engage in public political activity after having children.

Anarchists had diverse attitudes towrads motherhood and childcare. Most men and many women felt that woman's freedom meant the freedom to fulfill herself as a mother, with a natural responsibility for childbearing and often for education as well. They generally believed that women had the right to bear children outside marriage, and a few women went further, arguing for women's right to choose to have children outside an ongoing heterosexual relationship:

"As a freewoman, I refuse to bear children either to the state or to a man; I will bear them for myself and for my purpose ... My children shall be mine for my pleasure, until such time as they shall be their own for their own pleasure ..."

On the other hand, one woman wrote:

"Men must do childrearing if they are to become complete human beings instead of mere males, if children are to have the benefit of fathering as well as mothering, and if there is to be real equality between the sexes."

This was a rare viewpoint, though, and there is little evidence of men taking a substantial role caring for young children or of women suggesting they should do so. "Free motherhood" often proved socially and materially very difficult for those who tried it, though sometimes childcare was shared with other women. Older children were seen as more of a community responsibility, and men sometimes became involved in education, though less often than women.

Anarchist women were often involved in birth control campaigns, and some practised birth control or abortion themselves. Certainly, a number of women who were sexually involved with men and wished to remain politically active chose to have no children, or only one.

An anarchist manifesto of 1895, in the one line it gave to relations between the sexes, called for independence and co-operation in sexual as in industrial and economic relations. Many early communities were modelled on single sex settlements or religious orders. As the language of universal brotherhood or fellowship implies, women did not fit easily into this model, and were often seen as a potential source of disruption. In some communities, women joined as sexual partners, not as autonomous individuals. Single women faced particular problems and pressures both inside and outside the community.

The popular view of the anarchist belief in "free love" was that it meant constant orgies, and many visiting sightseers must have been disappointed. Although some anarchist men and a few women believed in having numbers of partners on the basis of sexual desire alone, for most free love meant something different: a (heterosexual) freely chosen monogamous commitment based on romantic love. If love died, in theory the partnership would end blamelessly. Unfortunately, love did not always die for both partners at the same time.

Women had more to lose than men in defying sexual convention in a society in which they were economically and socially unequal as well as being expected to be responsible for children. They sometimes found that what they meant and what men meant when they spoke of love or passion were quite

while men were theorising, women were actually trying to live out their theories

different. Those who didn't believe in monogamy found sexual jealousy doesn't go away that easily, and in practice the same old double standard of morality, one rule for men and another for women, often operated.

"Supported" by her Husband

"A man works from sun to sun, a woman's work is never done."

A cartoon from The Vote - *the Women's Social & Political Union paper*

George Barrett, editor of *The Anarchist*, wrote in 1913 that the fight for the vote was progressive, but the real war for women was in the home, with men. This was a conclusion many women had already reached. As one writer to *The Freewoman* acidly pointed pointed out, while men were theorising, women were actually trying to live out their theories. They did so with varying degrees of success. Edith Lees said in later life of her experiences at Fellowship House: "Fellowship is Hell; lack of Fellowship is heaven."

In urban communities, marriage or its equivalent often meant leaving. In rural communities, nuclear families tended to develop, leading an increasingly private existence within the colony. Some women, disillusioned with the gap between theory and practice, moved away from anarchist ideas altogether. But for others, however imperfect the reality compared with the ideals, the struggle for a new life was preferable to the conventional life they had left behind. They might leave one colony to found or join another, or to develop similar ideas in a more individual context. Their daughters and sons would, at least, struggle for change from a better vantage point.

Judy Greenway has been an active anarchist and feminist since the late 1960s. She currently teaches a course on utopias and utopianism at the University of East London, and is researching the history of anarchist women in the United Kingdom.

Colonising the Land: Utopian Ventures

COLIN WARD

I f a single slogan had to be chosen to epitomise the hopes of utopian ventures in twentieth century Britain, the words would be "Back to the Land". This is as true of communities of production, where the intention was to practice the crafts in combination with food production, as of communities of spiritual endeavour or of pacifism, where self-support depended on small-scale mixed farming. It was even true of the Garden City mpvement's aspirations, where the community is surrounded by market gardens and where the density of twelve houses to the acre gave "gardens of sufficient size to be of commercial value to the tenants ... and not too large to be worked by an ordinary labourer and his family".[1]

In the late nineteenth century the 'Land Question' had been one of primarily parliamentary politics rather than utopian hopes. 'The Drift from the Land', fuelled by the effects of the Enclosure Acts and the amalgamation of holdings, was a fact of British life. Britain was thought to be unique in Europe for having no peasants, and legislators promoted and protected the idea of the resettlement of the land for a century that ended only in 1982. All through the nineteenth century agitation for smallholding was linked with the campaign for allotments, resulting in ineffective legislation which empowered councils to provide both allotments and smallholdings for resale. But since most would-be smallholders were not in a position to enter into such commitments, and simply wanted to rent, it was correctly described as window dressing.

Does the aim of the restoration of the peasantry belong to the world of utopian communities, or was

Anarchist author Colin Ward details the history of the largest and longest lasting 'Back to the Land' venture in Britain.

[1]UNWIN, Raymond
(1909) *Town Planning
in Practice* Unwin,
London, p 320

[2]*The Penny Magazine
1845*, quoted by
Bridget WHEELER,
'Allotment hold'
Town & Country
Planning, Vol 60 1991
pp 168-9.

[3]McGREGOR, O R
(1961) *Introduction to
Lord Ernle. English
Farming Past and
Present*, 6th edition

it a matter of political expediency? Did the promoters of the ideal have different hopes from those of the people who experienced a whole series of policies towards land settlement? Were the settlers communitarians or rugged individualists? As long ago as 1845 it had been argued that the case for allotments was "moral rather than Economic".[2] Historian Martin J Wiener observed: "The less practically important rural England became, the more easily could it come to stand simply for an alternative and complimentary set of values, a psychic balance wheel". He cites the opinion of the sociologist O R McGregor that "the pathetic delusion that some sort of land settlement scheme contained the secret cure for the ills of industrial society had great survival value".[3]

It did not appear a pathetic delusion to the variety of charitable and propagandist organisations of a century ago, advocating the recolonisation of rural England. Quite apart from the desire to stem the 'drift from the land', there was a whole movement of revulsion against the horrors of Victorian industrial society and the hypocrisies of Victorian middle-class life, reflected in the Tolstoyan, socialist and anarchist movements of the time and the cult of the 'simple life'.

By 1908 the 'window dressing Acts' had only provided 244 holdings. It was the Small Holdings and Allotments Act of 1908 which, at last, enabled county councils to provide small holdings for rent.

It was in fact a very important piece of legislation. Eighty years later there are English counties where because of this Act the county council is the largest single landowner. County council small-holdings certainly met a long-felt need. They seldom addressed the aspirations that had surfaced unofficially for a community life on the land.

The First World War was a watershed in the aspirations for re-establishing a peasantry. Not only did it provide a short-lived viability for Britain's depressed agriculture and horticulture but it left an aftermath of desire for a life on the land. Lloyd George, as wartime Prime Minister, declared in a speech which,"epitomised, stimulated, and perhaps exploited" the land settlement idea, that "There must be a scheme for settling the gallant soldiers and sailors on the land ... The vast majority will return to their old occupations, But I am told that a good many of those who have been living an open-air life do not want to return to the close atmosphere of workshop and factory. If that is the case, they ought to have the opportunity of living on the land ...".[4]

In terms of aspirations this was certainly the case. Land came on to the market on a scale never known before. The pre-war introduction of death duties coupled with the slaughter of inheritors in the First World War resulted in a situation where, as Howard Newby put it, "In four years between 1918 and 1922 England, in the words of a famous *Times* leader of the day, 'changed hands'. One quarter of the area of England was bought and sold in this hectic period." Not very many of these transfers of ownership actually served the needs of the ex-soldiers for whom the Land Settlement (Facilities) Act of 1919 was intended. Its provisions had not had the anticipated effect even though these included farm colonies with central farms attached, profit-sharing farms and co-operative marketing.

Leah Leneman sought the recollections of settlers and their children in *Fit for Heroes?*[5]. "Those who had succeeded without previous agricultural experience," she found, "as characters of enormous grit and determination." In spite of the fact that their holdings were now supporting a third generation, to Robert Kirk and Bob Fraser, "the claim after World War I that ex-servicemen would be able to stand on their own two feet with just 'five acres and a cow' was a terrible con. Not that they thought those who formulated the policy had been insincere, but rather that it had been lunacy from the start although the ex-servicemen had believed what the government told them." The son of another responded that "It will be civil servants who dreamt that up, because they couldnae' have been practical men or they would never have gave anybody a holding of four acres say to make a living out of". Others of the second generation explained that their fathers survived with a second job, working at Parkhead or on the railway or for nearby farmers. "One holder with six acres was a stamp dealer and did well out of that." For others, how indeed did they manage? "There were two answers which applied to all the holdings, of whatever size? Firstly, they managed by unremitting backbreaking work. The second answer was the crucial participation of the women and children."

In England and Wales the direct intervention by central government in the provision of smallholdings for ex-servicemen came to an end in 1926. This was

[4]RUSSEL SMITH, Newlin (1946) *Land for the Small Man* King's Crown Press, London, p96

[5]LENEMAN, Leah (1989) *Fit For Heroes?* Aberdeen University Press, p20

....

It will be civil servants who dreamt that up, because they couldnae' have been practical men or they would never have gave anybody a holding of four acres say to make a living out of

....

[6]FARMER, John (1980) "The Growing Years" in *The Gardeners Companion & Diary* National Society of Leisure Gardeners, p16

[7]FRY, Joan Mary (1947) *Friends Lend a Hand in Alleviating Unemployment* Friends Book Centre, p34

also the year of the General Strike. The Religious Society of Friends, popularly known as the Quakers, in 1926, sought to find ways to alleviate the hardships endured by the miners. It found that some allotment gardens were going out of cultivation as plot-holders lacked even the money to buy seeds and fertilisers, and that men who did cultivate their allotments were penalised for unemployment pay because of the suspicion that they might be selling the produce. The Friends committee was enabled to get clear statements from the Ministry of Labour that the small amount of produce which a man could sell from his allotment would not affect the amount of his dole"[6], and as a result of appeals the Friends were able to provide seeds, seed potatoes, tools, fertiliser and lime. By the 1930s the Friends were exploring the possibilities of "Group Holdings" using a piece of land larger than an allotment but smaller than small holdings. This Group Holdings scheme began in county Durham in 1933 and within the next twelve months 16 groups were started in the North East, and "also took root in South Wales, Monmouthshire, Yorkshire, Derbyshire, Staffordshire, Nottinghamshire, Cumberland and Northumberland."[7] The significance of this Quaker initiative is that it laid the foundations for the longest lasting government sponsored venture in collective horticulture, the Land Settlement Association.

During the summer of 1933 a visitor called at Friends House to discuss a scheme which he had in mind. This was an experiment for moving unemployed industrial workers from Durham, providing them with full-time holdings of about five acres in another part of England, giving them training and providing marketing facilities, with a view to their becoming, in two or three years time, once more self-supporting citizens. This Gentleman (Mr - now Sir - Malcolm Stewart) said he had £25,000 which he wished to devote to this purpose, and he asked if the Friends Committee or the Central Allotments Committee would consider such a scheme, provided the government were willing to give a similar amount.

Consequently the Land Settlement Association (LSA) was formed in 1935 and at its first meeting the Minister of Agriculture announced "that money would be available up to £50,000 per year for three years."

The founders were aware that behind their venture was a history of disappointments, whether in "utopian" colonies, charitable enterprises, or the experiment in settling ex-servicemen on the land. They adopted four fundamental principles:

1   Assistance would be given only to group settlements, not to individual smallholdings.
2   Co-operative methods would be adopted for the purchase of smallholders requisites, the marketing of their produce, and the general working of the scheme.
3   Settlers, both men and their wives, would be carefully selected. In General the Association proposed to select men who had successfully cultivated allotments.
4   Adequate training and supervision would be given.

The Association tended to acquire estates in areas with an established tradition of market gardening (see map on page 28). A Characteristic LSA landscape emerged. There was a small home farm, usually the original farmstead, occupied by the supervisor or advisors, with central buildings for grading and packing of produce, and beyond it about forty holdings of around four to eight acres. The tenants' houses, each with a small front garden were built where possible on existing roads. Where necessary new access roads were laid out on a grid-iron layout. Close to the dwellings were glass-houses, pig sheds and chicken houses, followed by a patch for fruit and vegetable cultivation, and beyond that an area designed to be ploughed and harvested together with neighbouring plots, should this be necessary. Sometimes there was also a large-scale orchard.

It was not easy to assimilate a population of 150 to 200 newcomers with different habits and accents into the general life of quiet country districts, nor were the newcomers a ready-made community, since they were nearly all strangers to one another. Moreover physical facilities, especially schools, were often quite inadequate. Nor were the problems only external. To be a successful smallholder a man must have ambition, enterprise, unremitting industry, and a love of the land for its own sake, qualities which his wife must share. They must be prepared to work for long hours for an uncertain and irregular income. A long term history of industrial unemployment hardly tended to bring out such qualities.

· · · · · · · · · · · · · · · · · · · ·
The founders were aware that behind their venture was a history of disappointments, whether in "utopian" colonies, charitable enterprises, or the experiment in settling ex-servicemen on the land
· · · · · · · · · · · · · · · · · · · ·

[8]Recollection kindly provided by Martin Chapman, Hitcham, Suffolk in November 1991

[9]DUNN, Ted ed (1963) *Alternatives to War and Violence* J Clarke & Co, London

Joe Chapman was a plasterer in Hayes, Middlesex, unemployed for eighteen months, who applied for training at an LSA estate in Bedfordshire in 1938. His son explains that "When he went there he thought he was fulfiling his dream. He thought he was going to stay." But what was his dream? "I think that ultimately he was a romantic communist, probably a utopian socialist before that. What he read was books about *Island Farm* or *I Bought a Mountain*. He would really have liked to take over a deserted island." He was installed in an empty house on the LSA site and learned from the LSA advisers the secrets, not only of horticulture, but of goat culture. "By the time we arrived four months later, he was very happy and had all sorts of things to show us, and it was all very exciting. We moved into no-man's-land where there were rows of houses that were empty still, and by the time we left the Land Settlement tractors were ploughing it all up ... There were lots of advisors who he liked very much. There was a man who advised on pigs and a man who advised on glass-houses, and he enjoyed all that, but maybe he had a feeling that it was all going sour. By the end of the year he had cycled over to Suffolk and decided this was the place and had the great good luck to find this farm where the whole family has been ever since. It seems to me that we lived on tomatoes and goats milk for years. I dare say that my father was almost unique, apart from his neighbour who was a Welsh miner, in living out his dream of self-sufficiency on the LSA estate. I remember particularly the goats and the Angora rabbits. We all loved it."[8]

Another was Ted Dunn, a veteran of the Friends Ambulance Unit in the Second World War who became an LSA tenant in Essex in 1948 and has been there ever since. His son is a member of the growers co-operative that took over since the closure of the Association in 1983. In spite of his pioneering experiments in organic growing, watched with scepticism by his neighbouring growers, Ted Dunn is more readily associated with a whole series of books he has edited or written on the preconditions for world peace.[9] Pinned down on the question of whether his LSA estate at Foxash was a community, he replied, "It was a community of individuals, as you might expect. The original settlers had everything against them. The organisation was very poor. The soil was poor. The markets were against them ... My first main recollection from a community point of view was of harvesting ... because in those days you had twenty of us who would all join in together to stook, thrash

> I dare say that my father was almost unique, apart from his neighbour who was a Welsh miner, in living out his dream of self-sufficiency on the LSA estate

and all the rest. It was a kind of community. That only lasted a few years actually, for then the combines came in ... There were also the monthly meetings, and through having a central store, that was a wonderful place to meet other people."[10]

[10]Recollection kindly provided by Ted Dunn, Lawford, Essex in October 1991

By the early 1970s the average earnings of the Associations tenant's were well above the average agricultural wage. For some tenants, growing provided a good living. But this was subject to several qualifications. Some estates were more successful than others, and even on the same estate, some tenants were more skillful, more hardworking, or just luckier than others, or had been able to invest more in glass-houses and equipment, as encouraged by the Association's central office. In any case the income represented a 'family' wage, for it usually resulted from the labour of the tenant and his wife, and often their children. Earnings which depended on being able to pick, trim, wash, and package thousands of heads of celery in the early morning because one of the multiple stores was having a Celery Week, could not have been achieved otherwise.

[11]Statement by the Minister of Agriculture, December 1, 1982

The end of the Land Settlement Association was announced, just as Parliament went into its Christmas recess in 1982. The, then, Minister of Agriculture, Peter Walker, told the House of Commons that tenants should take over responsibility for marketing their produce, and that this should happen as quickly as possible. The decision covered the remaining ten estates, comprising 3,900 acres, with about 530 tenants, as well as about 300 staff. Tenants were allowed to purchase their holdings at half the current market price.[11] But the Ministry cut off any further short or long-term finance. Some of the growers cut adrift simply moved out, and their homes and land were sold on behalf of the Ministry during the property boom of the 1980s. The plain little houses were expanded into ranch-style homes and the land was either neglected or flourished as paddocks for horse owners. But at two estates at least - Foxash Growers Ltd in Essex and Newbourn Growers Ltd in Suffolk - genuine co-operatives were formed. The members continue to produce in an extremely specialised way for the retailing supermarkets, and at their behest the produce is picked in the early morning, washed, graded, trimmed, packaged and provided with the sellers label, bar-code and sell-by-date, ready for the truck. When questioned, the co-operative members, heavily dependant on bank loans, and at the mercy of the polices of a

Parts of this article previously appeared in: *The Raven; Anarchist Quarterly* March 1992; and *Freedom Press.*

handful of big customers, as well as the ever present possibility of crop failures, claim that they are more content than in the days of their dependency on the LSA. But these survivors felt bitter about the abrupt closure in 1982 and started legal proceedings against the Ministry claiming the LSA had been falsely presented as a sound investment and had run tenants into debt by selling produce at too low a price. The Ministry of Agriculture offered compensation of £6.5 million, cancellation of tenant's debts and all costs - whilst continuing to deny liability.

This was the messy end of the longest-lasting, largest-scale venture in getting "back to the land" in Britain, as well as the only one, apart from its precursors in resettling ex-servicemen, to be sponsored and funded by government. Could it be called "utopian" and could its estates be described as communities"? Undoubtedly its Quaker founders were seen as utopian even though they were conscious of experimenting, step-by-step, with measures to relieve unemployment. In ordinary political circles very few alternatives other than Keynesian public-spending programmes were being advocated in the 1930s. There is also some evidence that the men who were willing to commit themselves and their families to this leap into the countryside, far from home, were people who cherished the ideal of a return to the land. It is doubtful whether many were inspired by the concept of communal living. The Land Settlement Association was in retrospect, an attempt, and the largest ever made in Britain, to accommodate utopian ideals of recolonising the land, with the harsh realities of ordinary life. For its tenants there were few alternative choices.

Colin Ward is a veteran anarchist writer whose books tend to explore popular and unofficial uses of the environment. His Anarchy in Action *and* Talking Houses *are in print from Freedom Press, 84 Whitechapel High Street, London E1. His* Influences: Voices of Creative Dissent *comes from Green Books, and his classic* The Child in the City, *as well as* The Child in the Country *are available from NCVO, 8 All Saints Street, London N1.*

Brentham Estate - a new community

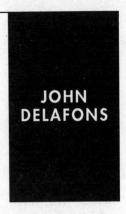

JOHN DELAFONS

When we had some friends to dinner recently at our house in Ealing, West London, they arrived a bit late. They explained that they had been visiting the nearby Brentham Estate. I had not realised that the estate, which features regularly in local estate agents' adverts, was anything special. But, in fact, as Peter Hall records in *Cities of Tomorrow*, it is (or should be) an icon in the early history of British town planning and housing. I decided to find out more about it.

The concept of new communities or new settlements has been taken up by a variety of protagonists in the past few years, as yet without any substantial results. That may be partly because, on their own, neither the profit motive nor aesthetic objectives provide sufficient stimulus. The history of the Brentham Estate reminds us of the idealism of the early days of town planning, and of its relationships to reformist movements in the economic, social and cultural fields. There was a vision and enthusiasm, combined with a practical ability to get things done, that seems to be missing today. Ebenezer Howard and Frederick Osborn had it, and so did the founders of the Brentham Estate.

Perhaps we can best conjure up the spirit of those days by recalling the events of 27 May 1911, ten years after Ealing Tenants Ltd was founded and began the development of what became the Brentham Estate.

On that day their Royal Highnesses the Duke and Duchess of Connaught arrived to declare open the Brentham Club and Institute. The Brentham Choral Society sang an ode to the Duke and Duchess. The

New communities were being created in urban areas as well. This fascinating article first appeared in the November/December 1992 edition of the magazine *Town & Country Planning*.

Duke praised the pioneering project and observed: "If we wish to keep our countrymen strong and moral, we must think of their houses." Other speeches followed, and Henry Vivian, the founder of Ealing Tenants and one of those splendidly tetchy and radical characters who feature in the history of town planning, seized the opportunity to lambast the Mayor for "the antediluvian character of some of the byelaws of Ealing Corporation", which in his opinion had obstructed the layout of the estate. The children then plaited the maypole; tennis, cricket, bowls and croquet were played on the Institute's ground; there were exhibitions of horticulture and by the women's woodworking class; and the day ended with dancing and non-alcoholic refreshment.

> **If we wish to keep our countrymen strong and moral, we must think of their houses**

All this in ten short years after Henry Vivian held the inaugural meeting in 1901 at a local pub - the Haven Arms. In that time farm land on the northern outskirts of Ealing had been bought and housing for about 1,500 people had been built. The estate was nearing completion.

Co-partnership contrast
The novelty of the project can only be appreciated against the background of other endeavours during the preceding century to provide decent housing for working men and their families. Those were basically of two kinds: the paternalistic and the philanthropic. The first category included such landmarks as New Lanark, Saltaire, Ackroyden, Bournville and Port Sunlight. They were all provided by industrialists for their workforce, with a view to keeping the workers healthy and productive. The second category was the big housing charities such as the Peabody Trust, which by 1864 had provided for 3,815 tenants in their sanitary but somewhat grim properties.

Henry Vivian (1863-1930) came from a quite different stable. He was a carpenter and trade unionist, with strong connections with the co-operative movement. As a young man he founded a building workers' co-operative in Pimlico, which by 1897 had 17 branches in London. One of these was in Ealing and, under Vivian's leadership, six members clubbed together to buy a plot of land for £400 and build themselves six houses. The members contributed £50 each and Vivian raised the rest of the £1,000 initial capital needed from various well-wishers, including Leopald de Rothschild, whose family at that time lived nearby at Gunnersbury House.

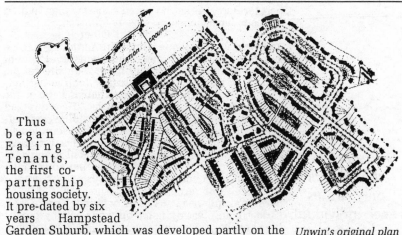

Thus began Ealing Tenants, the first co-partnership housing society. It pre-dated by six years Hampstead Garden Suburb, which was developed partly on the same principles. (Bedford Park is generally recognised as the first garden suburb, but despite its connections with the Arts and Crafts movement, it was a speculative development for the middle classes.)

Unwin's original plan for the Brentham Estate

Vivian later defined the three basic principles of co-partnership housing as tenant profit sharing, estate planning, and profit sharing by building employees. At the Brentham Estate, the houses were all owned by Ealing Tenants Ltd; the tenants paid rent but also held shares in the company. When they wanted to leave, they sold their shares back to the company at a price that reflected the increased value of the estate. It was a form of 'shared equity', but the equity was represented by the estate as a whole, in which the tenants owned a share. It evidently worked successfully at Brentham. By 1913, 510 houses had been completed and the company held property worth £158,000. Rents were 6/6 (33p) to 21/- (£1.05) a week excluding rates.

The first houses built by Ealing Tenants were a conventional terrace, probably taken from a builders' pattern book. But among the original objectives was: 'To provide for pastimes and pleasures of people within sight of their own homes; and by well ordered disposition of land give a family in a small house all the natural advantages of landscape and garden outlook, hitherto only possible to a man with large possessions.' in 1906 and 1907 the co-partnership bought more land, totalling about 60 acres. It was at this stage that the idea of a planned suburb took shape and Raymond Unwin was called in. He and his partner Barry Parker prepared a master plan, which seems to have have been closely followed.

Unwin wrote eloquently of the advantages to be gained by the kind of neighbourhood development made possible by co-partnership: 'The site can be thought of and planned as a whole ... the co-partnership principle marks a new era in housing and opens up a quite new range of possibilities.' He envisaged communal space and community buildings, conservation of 'spots of natural beauty' and distant views, and recreational and social facilities. 'The principle of sharing,' he wrote, 'not only causes each individual house to become more attractive, but gives to the whole area that coherence which springing from the common life of the community, expresses itself in the harmony and beauty of the whole.' Unwin and Parker themselves designed only one small group of four houses at Brentham. Most of the housing was produced by F Cavendish Pearson and by G Lister Sutcliffe, who had already been active at Letchworth. Much of it was in the Letchworth cottage style - hipped roofs, gables, dormer windows, good workmanship but no meretricious details. Even door numbers and letter boxes were part of the original designs. Most of the houses were in short terraces, designed to form a coherent group. Blank end walls were avoided by angled houses at road junctions. The overall layout was in the picturesque manner but included one more formal avenue, Brentham Way, in the Hampstead style. All the houses had gardens front and back, and most were grouped around internal spaces that were available as 'additional gardens'. A horticultural society was formed to instruct tenants on how to grow their own food.

> The principle of sharing not only causes each individual house to become more attractive, but gives to the whole area that coherence which springing from the common life of the community, expresses itself in the harmony and beauty of the whole

Waning philosophy

By 1914 the estate was substantially complete and in the form that exists today. What happened after that is a rather sad tale. The original co-partnership concept faded away and by 1930 Ealing Tenants was offering houses that became vacant for sale on the open market. In 1936 a controlling interest in Ealing Tenants was sold to the Liverpool Trust (a large housing association), who sold it on to the Bradford Property Trust in 1940. Ealing Tenants changed from being a friendly society to become a private company, and henceforth the estate was run on commercial lines. In 1950 the policy of allowing tenants to buy at favourable prices was discontinued. The institute became a private club, open to non-tenants, and a licence for the sale of alcohol was obtained. That marked the end of the estate's original philosophy.

During its brief history from 1900 to 1914 the housing co-partnership concept gained many adherents. In 1913 the Garden Cities and Town Planning Association listed 58 garden suburb developments, of which 38 were run wholly or partly on co-partnership lines. But after the Great War a number of factors led to the decline of the co-partnership movement. Local authorities were given new housing powers and became the prime providers of rented housing, while speculative housebuilders developed new and much cheaper types of housing for sale, which led to the vast suburban estates of the 1930s. The natural pride in homeownership and the bad reputation of private landlordism seemed to render the co-partnership concept obsolete.

Revival of Interest

A revival of interest in the Brentham Estate as a distinctive neighbourhood with an interesting history became apparent after the 1967 Civic Amenities Act. The Brentham Society was founded to encourage the protection and maintainance of the estate. In 1969 it became a Conservation Area, and the Ealing Planning Department published a helpful booklet designed to conserve the original architectural character of the estate, and discourage "ill-advised improvements". The Brentham Society continues to encourage the appreciation of the estate and has assembled a fascinating oral history from the recollections of early residents. In 1987, following the great storm, it raised some £1,500 and planted 90 new trees. In 1990 it reprinted the booklet that was originally published in 1912 to commemorate the visit of the Duke and Duchess of Connaught with which this article began. The sense of community is now restored. The history of Brenthan Estate recalls the idealism and the charm of the early days of town planning. It reminds us that in those early days planning was concerned with the improvement of housing conditions and the cultivation of neighbourhood identity and community well being, with educational and recreational oppourtunities for all. The housing co-partnership idea was closely allied to early town planning concepts, which found their expression in Brentham, Letchworth and other developments before the public sector and speculative suburban housebuilders took over. We need to recapture some of that early idealism, enthusiasm and practical vigour if the concept of new settlements is to be revived.

The Brentham Society can be contacted care of: Tony Oliver, 48 Denison Road, London W5 1NV

The Pioneer Co-Partnership Suburb (1912) Reprinted by Brentham Society,1990

JOHNSON, B (1977)*Brentham:Ealing's Garden Suburb* Brentham Society

TIMMS, M *Ealing Tenants Ltd - pioneers of Co-partnership Housing* Ealing Local History Society

HALL, P (1988) *Cities of Tomorrow* Basil Blackwell, Oxford

John Delafons is an Associate of the Department of Land Economy at Cambridge University and a Council Member of the Town and Country Planning Association. *He was formerly Deputy Secretary at the Department of Environment responsible for Planning and Inner Cities, including New Towns and new communities.*

Eric Gill: 1882 - 1940

Controversial sculptor, wood engraver, typographer, socialist, catholic and communard. He lived in communities at Ditchling Common in Sussex (1913 - 24); Capel-y-ffin in Wales (1924 - 28) and Pigotts in Buckinghamshire (1928 - 1940). John Bradbrook shares some thoughts on the man.

*W*hen I was asked to write a few words for this book on Eric Gill it seemed a bit odd. All that I could remember about him at first, from reading a review of Fiona MacCarthys biography, was that he had a somewhat incestious relationship with his daughters. This did not seem to fit well with late twentieth century ideas of "political correctness" with which Diggers and Dreamers positively oozes. It is also an interesting example of how in the world of instant mass communication it is possible to have a "little knowledge" about all sorts of things without really knowing about them.

So I went to get Fiona Mac-Carthy's biography and Gill's own autobiography out of the library to find out more. To clear up the point about incest, his relationship with his daughters was more physical than it ought to have been, though it did seem to stop short of outright sex. He did have a long term physical relationship with Gladys, one of his sisters, though. There was however much more to Eric Gill than that. He did live for many years in large communal households, in Sussex, Wales, the Pyrenees and deepest Buckinghamshire. These outfits, though, did tend to have him as a central figure.

He did hold to his ideals of the

simple life, the "back to the land" philosophy, the dignity and integrity of manual labour and his personal stand against mass production industrial society. The bakery near where he lived as a child which produced " machine made bread remained as a symbol of what he was against. Yet he managed, also, to

be a famous artist and sculptor who, in addition, designed a number of well known type faces. He sculpted the Stations of the Cross at Westminster Cathedral. So there is hope for us all yet, being involved in a communal lifestyle need not be a barrier to fame!

Gill certainly had a great zest for life and was certainly seen by many of his contempories as "a larger than life character". In his younger days he was an active socialist. In those far off times (before 1917) it was perhaps easier to believe that socialism would be "the best of all possible worlds".

"... industrial methods of production reduce the worker to a subhuman condition ... it makes good mechanics, good machine minders, but men and women who in every other respect are morons, cretins, semi-imbeciles, for whom crossword puzzles, football competitions, watered beer, sham half-timbered bungalows, Burns & Oates church statues, slimming and film stars are the highest form of amusement."[1]

Yet for Gill, socialism was too dry and unemotional a creed. So he converted to Catholicism, which was for him, perhaps, more imaginative and sensual. Also Heaven had the advantage over

New Age , 1907 style. A masthead which Gill designed for a journal of that name.

the late (and generally unlamented) Soviet Union, that nobody could actually visit the place (as André Gide visited the USSR in the Thirties reporting back that it was not in fact all that it was cracked up to be). Yet Gill never lost his mischievous sense of fun, making statues of

the Madonna and putting necklaces on them for example.

His attitude to women was deeply ambivalant. He was certainly keen on them! Much of Fiona MacCarthy's book is about his convoluted relationships with them. Some of his ideas could perhaps be described as "feminist" in orientation, such as the importance of the domestic side of life and of everyday household tasks - baking bread for example. Yet in other ways he acted very much like a typical Victorian patriarch. His casual and exploitative relationship with the family's live-in maid, Lizzie, while his wife Ethel was having their first child, does leave a nasty taste. He also seemed to think that women could not be artists and that true creativity was essentially a masculine activity.

Despite all this, what I have read of Eric Gill has definitely left me with a positive view of the man. It is impossible to do justice to somebody who led such a full, active and creative life in a few words. If you want to find out more, then get hold of a copy of Fiona MacCarthy's biography or indeed of Gill's book on himself. An excess of modesty was not one of his problems!

"What I hope above all things is that I have done is something towards re-integrating bed and board, the small farm and the workshop, the home and school, earth and heaven."[2]

[1]GILL, Eric (1937) *Money and Morals* Faber & Faber, London, p20
[2]Eric Gill quoted by **Fiona MacCARTHY**, p vii. See below.
Selected bibliography
MacCARTHY, Fiona (1989) *Eric Gill* Faber & Faber, London
GILL, Eric (1940) *Autobiography* Jonathan Cape, London
GILL, Evan (1947) *Eric Gill: Workman* Devin-Adair, London
SPEIGHT, R (1966) *The life of Eric Gill* Methuen, London
YORKE, M (1981) *Eric Gill Man of Flesh and Spirit* Constable, London

The Homesteads, Stirling 1910 - 1975

*I*t can't be many people who when they tell their parents that they are going to join an alternative community get the reaction that Catriona Stamp of People in Common got - "Oh well it runs in the family!"

Her maternal Great Grandparents, it turns out, lived at a virtually unknown co-operative garden suburb in Stirling.

The Homesteads grew from a coalition of radical Scottish groups active at the turn of the century, the Independent Labour Party, the Stirling Co-operative Society, the Scottish Guild of Handicraft,the Quakers and the Garden City movement.

Following a number of meetings in Stirling on such topics as "Co-operation in House Building" and "The Future of the City", and following a report by the local Trades Council to a Royal Commission on housing it was proposed to set up a co-operative homesteads project as a way of solving the problem of overcrowded and unsanitary working class housing in Stirling.

On the intiative of the local council a group consisting of ten families was formed, who finally moved into the homesteads - a collection of smallholdings on the edge of Kings Park in Stirling. They are probably the only housing co-operative ever to be situated on Crown property.

The group were registered with the Scottish Registrar of Friendly Societies with the aims "to carry on the trade of buying, selling, hiring and letting lands and buildings and to carry on the trades of builders; also to carry on the industries or businesses of farmers, market gardeners, horticulturalist, nurserymen, poultry farmers, wholesale and retail dealers in farm and garden produce and agricultural implements" - a list that probably sums up the activities of a large number of present day communities

Like many present day communities they were also beset by financial problems and personality clashes). But the community weathered the traumas and crises of the 1920s and 1930s and survived virtually intact as a co-partnership housing association until the Crown forced it out of existence in 1975.

Although, by then, very little of the early profit sharing co-operative scheme that Catriona's mother remembers visiting, as a small child, remained.

For a more detailed history of the Stirling Homesteads see:
AITKEN, P; CUNNINGHAM, C; and McCUTCHEON, B (1984) *Notes for a New History of Stirling: The Homesteads - Stirling Garden Suburb* published by the authors.

Pacifist Islands in a Martial Sea

ANDREW RIGBY

T he outbreak of war on September 3 1939 came as a profound disappointment to pacifists and presented them with a severe moral dilemma. Prior to the war their rôle had been clear - to try and avert war. But now, what could they do? How to reconcile the promptings of the pacifist conscience with the sense of duty owed to one's fellow citizens and neighbours?

Many responded by relinquishing their commitment to oppose war and made themselves available for conscription in the armed forces. Others attempted to reconcile their conscience with their sense of civic duty by serving in the Non-Combatant Corps where they were not obliged to carry weapons. Others resisted conscription and claimed the status of conscientious objector before the tribunals that were established. In the majority of cases where the sincerity of the individual's objection to conscription and war was accepted, the person was directed to perform some kind of 'alternative service' such as working on the land. Thus, by 1940 there was a steady supply of young men made available for agricultural work. Many of these young idealists found it difficult to find work, however, due to the reluctance of farmers to employ 'conchies' who were not only morally suspect but also invariably unskilled in the techniques of farming and agricultural work.

To help deal with this problem a scheme known as the Christian Pacifist Forestry and Land Units had been organised to enable groups of religious pacifists to live together communally whilst working on the land. Then, in December 1940, a conference was held where it was resolved to purchase some farm land

During World War II, while the world sank deeper into violence and barbarism, groups of pacifists and conscientious objectors were enthusiastically establishing rural communes as part of an effort to sow the seeds of a new moral and social order for the post-war world. This article recounts something of their story.

[1] WELLOCK, Wilfred (1961) *Off the Beaten Track*, p70

where pacifists could be trained in agricultural techniques. By the Spring of 1941 a 309 acre farm at Holton Beckering in Lincolnshire had been bought for this purpose.

The initiative for this venture came from a group of influential pacifists within the Peace Pledge Union (PPU - the main pacifist organisation in Britain, founded 1934 and still active today). People like Eric Gill, Max Plowman, John Middleton Murry and Wilfred Wellock argued that at a time when the world was bent on destruction, it was the duty of the pacifist to bear witness to a higher order of morality and civilisation. They urged pacifists to join together in co-operative communities that might act as seedbeds of a new civilisation. In the words of Wilfred Wellock, the key role of the pacifist was 'to envisage the future and to seek ways and means of saving and introducing those values without which human existence ceases to have any meaning'. (*Peace News*, June 14 1940) The fulfilment of such a prophetic rôle required a 'politics of creative living'. The origins of war lay in our whole way of life and the materialistic values upon which it was based. Therefore the pacifist project must be to transform society from the bottom upwards. Wars would cease not so much when people refused to fight but when people had learned how to live.

For people like Wilfred Wellock these were exciting days, as he recorded in his autobiography:

"In the midst of the biggest and most devastating war in history, steps were being taken to build a more stable and enduring civilisation on new foundations. By 1941 I was devoting all my time to this purpose. Every month I spent several days at Holton Beckering to help in its work, and strengthen the faith of the men working there. In addition I visited as many of the new communities spread about the country as I could, and in the meantime wrote articles for Peace News, in whose pages Middleton Murry and I were perpetually expounding the wider aims and implications of the community concept.[1]

In March 1941 *Peace News*, the weekly newspaper of the PPU, began publishing a monthly supplement devoted to the coverage of community projects and the discussion of the ideas behind them. Those pacifists who felt unable to commit themselves to the communal life within an agriculturally based community were urged to develop the community spirit with friends through the establishment of income sharing networks. Even though they might be living

it was the duty of the pacifist to bear witness to a higher order of morality and civilisation. They urged pacifists to join together in co-operative communities that might act as seedbeds of a new civilisation

in an urban environment, they could still be pioneers working to develop a co-operative and non-exploitative alternative to capitalism.

The Gloucester Land Scheme was just one of the small-scale rural experiments in laying the foundations of a new order. It consisted of around half-a-dozen pacifists housed in a converted sports pavilion near Hempsted on the outskirts of Gloucester. A local Quaker had loaned the group the land upon which they grew vegetables and aspired to self-sufficiency. One of their number in 1941 was Tim Carlile, who recalled how

"... after the first year the Land Scheme working members were self-supporting and self-governing. Weekly meetings of the working members would decide domestic matters regarding the communal accommodation, catering, house-keeping and budgeting, and with one or two co-opted advisers the work to be done, the crops to be grown, marketing and overall finances. All work and responsibility for individual or special tasks were performed communally or by rota and some emphasis was placed on communal social activity, contacts, visits and exchange of produce, ideas and personnel with the wider community movement, and outside activities."

A similar small scale experiment was the Kingston Community Farm, founded by a group of pacifists from Kingston-upon-Thames, who purchased three acres of land at Charney Bassett in Berkshire in 1940. Rectory Farm housed two families and their children. Moore Place, near Stanford-le-Hope in Essex, was on a slightly larger scale: twelve members, 15 acres and two cows! Perhaps not untypically, the predominantly middle class members of this community had no agricultural experience prior to joining. Like others before and since they believed that what they lacked in practical experience could be compensated by their social idealism. It would appear from available records, however, that their vision of a new order did not extend to the sexual division of labour. As one visitor to Moore Place reported: on entering the house there was to be found the "women of the community preparing supper, ironing, washing, darning!" (*Peace News*, 16 May 1941).

Matters seem to have been organised somewhat differently at the Elmset Community, a 41 acre farm near Ipswich. There it would appear that tasks were shared by all the dozen or so members, regardless of sex. Founded in 1939, the original statement of the aims and the basis of the community is fairly typical

> **Wars would cease not so much when people refused to fight but when people had learned how to live.**

[2] "The Elmsett Community", *The Plough*, Summer 1939, vol 2, no 2, p 45

[3] DUNCAN, R (1964) *All Men Are Islands*, p 230

of the kind of philosophy that underpinned these attempts at social transformation.

> *"We realise that it is useless to try to re-design the super-structure of the old system while the foundations are at fault, and have decided that we must help to lay the foundations of a new order based on the principles of brotherhood and co-operation of all mankind. We therefore renounce the selfishness of the old order, and this can only be done by sharing our life together in a true community, working not for personal reward, but for the benefit of the whole, and holding all our material goods in common. Thus personal ambition will be relinquished for the higher ideal, and the individual personality freed from the warping effects of commercialism, will be able to express itself more fully in furthering that ideal.[2]"*

Unfortunately, the lived experience of those seeking to establish the nuclei of a qualitatively new civilisation was to prove rather more problematic than the theory had led them to expect. Too many pacifists living in community during the Second World War suffered from the illusion that people have only to resolve on perfection in order to achieve it.

The saga of Ronald Duncan's community in North Devon serves to illustrate some of the problems and tensions encountered by these pioneers of a new way of living. Duncan's account is replete with examples of what he portrayed as 'the depths of stupid childishness to which so many moderately intelligent people are brought when they are involved in any sort of communal activity.'[3] During the first year of the venture the 'hotch-potch of intellectual nitwits' (Duncan's description, not mine) revealed themselves to be strong on rhetoric and theory, rather weak on practice. It seemed to Duncan that once the novelty of the new way of life wore off, much of the work took on the character of routine chores which members sought to avoid - with the result that pigsties went uncleaned, tools unsharpened and milking delayed. When Duncan attempted to supervise the others to ensure that tasks were performed, he was charged with spying and behaviour contrary to the true spirit of community. He bemoaned the fact that anarchistic young pacifists who rejected any externally imposed discipline on ideological grounds, appeared to believe that there was something bourgeois in being tidy and punctual and that good manners was a sign of self-repression. There was also the problem of the 'free-riders', those people who came and stayed in the community without contributing to its upkeep in any way. Towards the end of his salutary experience Duncan concluded that 'as a community the experiment looked like a failure; but so were the social patterns around us failures too. At least we were not dropping bombs on each other.'[4]

[4]DUNCAN, p 249

[5]MIDDLETON MURRY, J (1952) *Community Farm*, p 52

[6]MURRY, pp 110-111

John Middleton Murry's experience was comparable to Duncan's. He purchased a 183 acre farm in Suffolk in 1942. He too noticed 'a strange carelessness amounting to a resentment of order' amongst the membership.[5] As in the case of so many community projects, interpersonal stresses and divisions caused by emotional jealousy and all the other small yet significant aspects of communal living were compounded by the development of factions formed around other issues to do with how the farm should be managed, how the finances should be organised, how the tasks should be allocated. As with communities before and since, the farm seemed to attract more than its fair share of oddballs and eccentrics - people who seemed to be motivated more by the desire to escape the constraints and responsibilities of the mundane world than by a positive vision of how to remake that world. As with so many utopian communities, the idealism of the truly committed made them easy prey for the parasitism of those seeking refuge from the demands of conventional existence.

In his history of conscientious objection during the Second World War Dennis Hayes identified three types of people who were attracted to the agricultural colonies: those with a definite 'calling' to work on the land with others; those who were seeking an escape; and those who needed a job during war-time. Murry's experience of all three types led him to the conclusion that the majority were primarily of the third category - those for whom, however much they might profess devotion to the idea and practice of community, farm life was a convenient way to spend one's time during a difficult period. He expressed his view of the human resources upon which the pacifist communities had to draw with characteristic forthrightness:

as a community the experiment looked like a failure; but so were the social patterns around us failures too - at least we were not dropping bombs on each other

"*Young pacifists are suspect. Unless by their works they definitely prove the contrary it may be assumed that the majority of them are seeking to escape social responsibility, though they may be unconscious of it. They made poor material for a long term effort. Half of them, as soon as the war was over, went back eagerly to their pre-war jobs: the vocation for co-operative agriculture which they had professed was merely an alibi.*"[6]

[7]**HAYES, D** (1949)
*Challenge of
Conscience*, p 217

Dennis Hayes was a little more charitable in his overall assessment when he admitted that..

"...the best thinkers (and talkers) were not always the best workers ... The pattern of community life imposed a strain that many were untrained to bear: the fundamental need was for self-discipline, and though the "communiteers" had often seen the Promised Land from afar, their provision for the journey was often sketchy in the extreme."[7]

What are we to make of this period of community building and its demise? In part the 'death' of many of the ventures has to be located within the general decline in the vitality of the British peace movement in the immediate post-war period. It was not just a case of pacifists deserting the valiant venture in order to pick up the threads of their interrupted careers and lives. The end of the war brought severe divisions and disputes within the pacifist movement. The disclosure of the full extent of the holocaust, the growing awareness of the terrible power that could be wielded by totalitarian states over civil society, and the revelation of the awesome destructive violence of atomic weapons, caused a number of pacifists to re-evaluate their position. Was non-violence a feasible stance against totalitarianism and all the forces of repression available to the modern state? How relevant was the individual's refusal to participate in war-making in the atomic age? These were the kinds of questions that exercised pacifists in Britain in the immediate post-war period - and planting the seeds of a new civilisation through the practice of exemplary non-violent, co-operative lifestyles had little place in the discourse.

Andrew Rigby wrote Alternative Realities *and* Communes in Britain - *two of the best known works on communal living in the 1970s. He has taught in the Department of Peace Studies at the University of Bradford since 1976 where his research has reflected his interest in exploring the potentialities of non-violence as a means of social change and reconstruction. He has been closely associated with* Peace News *and in recent years has been the co-ordinator of the Middle East Network/Work Group of War Resisters International.*

Indeed, when the post-war wave of communes emerged in the late 1960s few of these who participated in the movement knew much about their predecessors in the 1940s. As a researcher of and participant in the movement to create an 'alternative society' I remember the surprise I experienced when I came across the reports of the pacifist community projects of the Second World War. I can also remember the wonder of discovering that, despite all the differences in terminology and vocabulary between the two generations, they were essentially talking about the same prophetic role of those with the courage to translate their principles into practice and seek to live the utopian life of the future in the here-and-now.

Long may the tradition survive and persist!

Some Community Building Principles

LAURENCE BRIGHTBART

The American author M Scott Peck has extensive experience as a psychiatrist, a government administrator (he worked in the Office of the Surgeon General of the US Army), a group therapist, a lecturer, a parent and a spouse. In his book, *The Different Drum*, he describes four stages which groups go through. He calls these stages steps towards genuine community. Peck's concept of genuine or 'true' community is a desired state of being and communication for a particular group of people to aspire towards. The group may be an organisation - including 'living together' communities like those featured in *Diggers and Dreamers* - or a workshop specifically held to build community together.

Stage One: Pseudo-community
This is the stage of politeness. People are more concerned with getting on with each other than with a desire for genuine communication. People avoid their differences. Resentments and other unexpressed feelings usually bubble and seethe beneath the surface, until inevitably, there is an eruption into:

Stage Two: Chaos
There is no stopping the experience of chaos for a group that is intending to allow community to emerge within itself. This is not a "bad" stage. Chaos is not the breakdown of 'society' or 'community' that many people fear it is, as long as there is sufficient and genuine desire for community to be built.

Chaos is a time when individuals, far from avoiding differences, emphasise them. People attack, rescue or try to convert each other in an effort to obliterate differences. This is where people's

The process of community building which M Scott Peck describes is not the kind described earlier in relation to Lightmoor, but a method of reaching a desired state of group relating. This article describes the four stages and gives some characteristics of 'genuine community'

favourite solutions to problems will be offered, whether asked for or not.

Stage Three: Emptiness

Chaos can often be a very bruising time. At some point, enough people will have wearied of the unconstructive bickering and fighting that happens during it to be willing to give up, to let go of their favourite solutions, prejudices and judgements about people. They see that it's not working. People may feel that they are further from a state of community than they have ever been. They may be despairing of ever reaching community. People literally give in, or give up at this point.

People begin to sense what it is they do, or fail to do, that is creating a barrier between themselves and the others in the group. They start to accept responsibility for what they are experiencing. This allows a deliberate release, or emptying, to take place, of whatever seems to be in the way of simply being here with the group. People finally stop struggling with one another. All of this may happen openly, with individuals saying or showing emotionally what is going on for them. Or it may happen privately, in silence, as individuals see what they need to empty themselves of, and actively allow it to happen. Openly or privately, the key is willingness to give in and go through the sometimes painful, sometimes joyful (usually both!) experience of emptying oneself of a personal agenda, judgements, expectations, in fact anything which is a barrier to an experience of com-

Genuine community:

... *is inclusive and accepting. Individual differences are celebrated, and "soft" individualism (rather than "rugged") can flourish.*

... *is safe and confessional. It creates a "safe place" where brokenness, heroism and gifts are acknowledged.*

... *is realistic and multi-dimensional. Each member is free to express his or her facet of reality. There is an opportunity to express both the darkness and the light.*

... *facilitates healing and converting - once its members stop trying to heal and convert one another!*

... *manifests a palpable community spirit. That is, you can feel it.*

... *is contemplative and introspective. Its members are progressively learning to be empty and hence are progressively learning to be responsive to the spirit - to speak when they feel moved, and to be silent when feeling stilled.*

... *is a group of all leaders who share equal responsibility for and commitment to maintaining its spirit. And it is an ideal decision making body.*

... *is a group whose members can fight gracefully.*

munity with fellow group members. So a critical number of individuals empty themselves in this way, the atmosphere becomes softer, there is more respectful listening, more expression of vulnerablility, of feeling of brokenness, shared personal stories of tragedy and heroism, and more compassion.

Stage Four: Genuine (or true) Community
Chaos thus leads to community through emptiness. This to my mind is one of the most fundamental principles of community building. Scott Peck writes that the only other way out of chaos is into organisation; and this has been the way of most groups. We do need organisation of course. It's just that an organisation created to avoid chaos succeeds only at the cost of also avoiding the safety and creativity of true community.

To summarise, a group's members need to allow themselves to experience chaos, and go through it via the process of emptying, into community. Groups in community are able to experience long periods of restful, nourishing silences and a sense of safety. People may still fight, but because of the shared and often painful experience of building community together, and the shared investment in maintaining its presence, there is much greater willingness for people with opposing viewpoints not only to forcefully express them, but to actively, respectfully and effortfully listen to and understand their potential opponent's point of view. This is because in community, the desire for a workable, creative outcome is greater than the desire to prove oneself right. (Peck calls this 'fighting gracefully'!)

Most of us in our various groups and communities will have experienced being stuck in pseudo-community, no one daring to voice true thoughts or feelings. Or in chaos, bitching or trying to solve other people's problems. None of these experiences is bad or implies any failure for a group intending to build and maintain itself as a genuine community. One of the main differences between groups that are experienced in community building and maintenence, and those that aren't is simply that experienced groups are more skilled and therefore much quicker at acknowledging and responding to the fact that they are no longer 'in community'. They can see that something has gone out of balance and act to correct it. The less experienced group may see that something has gone wrong, but doesn't know quite what it is, or what to do to put it right.

· · · · · · · · · · · · · · · · · · · ·
"fighting gracefully"
· · · · · · · · · · · · · · · · · · · ·

Laurence Brightbart is involved in Community Building In Britain. *Details of the organisation can be found in the Resources section.*

Like Thieves in the Night

*L*ike the trusting progressives we are ("children are innocent, men are good, women are better"), we never worried overmuch at The Lodge about the possibilities of theft.

And this wasn't only a question of blind trust. After all, what burglars want to bother driving miles into the depths of the countryside, risking desperate collisions with rabbits, badgers and sheep, just on the off-chance that a bunch of ex-hippies might have something worth stealing?

When our neighbours down the lane invited us to join the new Neighbourhood Watch Scheme, opinion in the house was sharply divided. None of us felt in any danger and no one had any intention of doing any watching, but Sue argued that it would be the sociable thing to do, a kind of community relations exercise.

Pam agreed. "Look," she said, "it's people getting together, talking about community concerns. They even have pig roasts!"

But Jimmy, the Scottish anarchist vegetarian civil servant, unmoved by the thought of pig roasts, was implacaby opposed. "They're nothing more than vigilantes," he declared. "It's one step away from shopping your mother to the Thought Police! Pretty soon we'll have Guardian Angels on the weekly bus to Borchester!"

Bill, who tends to home in unerringly on the most progressive possible line to avoid being outflanked from the left, backed Jimmy to the hilt. "After all," he reminded the meeting, "don't we all believe that property is theft?"

No one really had any answer to that, but when the meeting broke up, the usual drift away to private spaces to watch private televisions or listen to private stereos had a slightly furtive air.

And so, as in carefree generations past, doors and windows continued to be left open at night, lightbulbs burned liberally in the corridors so that burglars wouldn't bark their shins and house contents insurance was for people who swallowed the capitalist line.

This Arcadia was rudely shattered just after Christmas when the unthinkable happened: burglars struck in the dead of night.

And struck to some effect: off went the communal television and video, a large collection of video tapes with labels such as "Carl 1" and "Jimmy 3", an even larger collection of Van Morrison albums, a 12-pack of orange juice cartons (minus one) and - adding insult to injury - an assortment of carefully-wrapped birthday presents for Sarah, whose birthday it had no doubt just become when the raid occurred.

Next morning, a Sunday, awareness was slow to dawn. When little Christabel woke up Joan and Carl at 7.0 am to complain that she couldn't watch cartoons because the television wasn't there, it never occurred to them that the child might be conveying a literal truth.

"You've probably got the wrong channel," mumbled Joan before

the point, Jake's room is next to the communal telly room where a gleaming new TV and video had been installed with curious swiftness - "for the children," of course.

Jake, whose heroes range from Richard Rogers (the architect, not the composer of "Victory at Sea") through Jeff Koons to Clint Eastwood, and who favours macho leather jackets and shades combined with Doc Martens painted in hammerite green on his 5'4" frame, is nothing if not combative at the best of times. But he was convinced that the burglars were going to return, head straight for his room and, disappointed at finding only 468 bound back copies of Domus and Design International, kill him.

"What if they torture me?" he quavered. "I'm a wimp! I'll never be able to stand it!"

To our shame, we took this at first as a joke. But Jake's paranoia grew worse. The slightest sound - the wind in the trees or a mouse gnawing happily on the wiring behind the skirting board - would bring him awake and shivering, terrified by the complicated rhythm of his own heartbeat until he realised it was coming from the stereo headphones lying discarded by his pillow.

We only began to take him seriously on a cold winter morning some weeks later. With darkness barely lifting outside, Jake heard a noise, sprang awake, forgot to check the time, and rushed stark naked into the kitchen brandishing the hedge strimmer and shouting, "All right, you bastards - make my day!"

"I don't know if he would have frightened off the burglars," said Ken, who had been peacefully preparing his breakfast. "But he put the fear of God into me!"

she sank back into sleep, leaving Christabel to ponder on the transparent stupidity of grown-ups.

When Bill wandered down for breakfast, he was appalled to find a lone carton of orange juice sprawled on the sacrosanct surface of the quarter-size snooker table in the front hall.

For Bill, violation of the snooker table is a crime comparable to sniping at innocent civilians in Bosnia or writing The

Drawing by Catriona Stamp

Satanic Verses - despite the fact that the table's surface is so completely warped that a ball struck slowly towards the bottom right-hand pocket is in more danger of disappearing bottom left.

Bill immediately snatched the offending object off the baize - thereby destroying, as Police Constable Julie was later to point out, the only chance the police might have had for fingerprint evidence. "It's not our fault that the clear-up rate on house burglaries is less than 20%," said Julie accusingly; "it's people like you!"

Indeed, PC Julie was conspicuous for a business-like lack of sympathy throughout the morning as the police strolled around The Lodge looking curiously at the shabby communal furnishings and the smartly-decorated private spaces, trying to look casual as they gave the odd sniff in corners and wastebins where drugs might have been if we hadn't collectively banned them more than a decade ago.

And Julie was clearly enjoying, not just the Orange Dazzler tea and leftover Christmas cake, but the irony of being invited to roam at will through the premises of people who had stumped up thousands of pounds in their time to support such anti-police organisations as the NUM, the Anti-Poll Tax Crusade or the workers at GCHQ.

Needless to say, the clear-up rate on house burglaries was never in danger of being improved in our case. And once the initial anger and guilt receded (Joan, the humanistic psychotherapist, reminded us that victims always feel guilt), we were left with a rising sense of paranoia that turned the next house meeting into a seminar on locks, bolts and, for those who had just seen Robert Redford in Sneakers, the electronics of crime prevention in the modern world.

And locks were soon acquired, significantly adding to tensions in the house as a spate of late-returning communards took to banging angrily on the front door at two in the morning. "Key? What key?"

But no one was more paranoi than Jake, one of only two com munity members whose bedro was on the ground floor. Mor

Income Pooling at Twin Oaks

**PAM
DAWLING**

In mainstream society, money is no longer just a token of exchange, a way of 'storing' value which can be redeemed later for products or services which are truly valuable in themselves. The accumulation of money itself has become a goal. Within the alternative society many people are looking for ways to avoid this glorification of money and so have set up various kinds of alternative economies (LETS, work credit systems, direct barter and so on). Income pooling is part of this movement to value people's work directly and equally rather than using money as an exchange medium.

Here at Twin Oaks I've been finding out how income pooling can work very well indeed for a large group (85 adults and 15 children), using a labour credit system and clear agreements about money. Each member is required to do a quota of tasks recognisable as work (generally 44 to 47 hours per week). This includes some income generating work such as making hammocks or rope chairs, or working in the tofu or book-indexing businesses, as well as providing all the services such as childcare, cooking, accounting, building maintenance, meeting facilitation and gardening. The community can then budget the labour available for the year, after guessing how many members there will be. The expected income can be calculated and the money budgeted accordingly. Once a year, in November, the Planners (a group of three members who serve for 18 months) draw up a draft economic plan including all the regular baseline expenses as well as requests for labour hours and money for each work area submitted by the Managers. After the baseline expenses are deducted , the remaining money and time available to fund the various on-going work areas of the com-

In her search for a secular, egalitarian community sharing land, work and income among a large group of people, Pam Dawling left her home of ten years at Lifespan (and the *D&D* editorial team) for Twin Oaks in Virginia, USA. Here she outlines the income pooling system used by Twin Oaks.

munity, together with special one-time projects, is put on the yearly Trade-Off Game. Each member gets a printed list of all the budget requests and has the chance to divide up the total of money and time available among the various areas and special projects, creating their own model budget for the community. This gives everyone the opportunity to 'vote' in favour of funding for the kind of lifestyle they choose. To make the budgets balance each person must choose between higher personal allowances or more in the garden budget or more donations to political causes for example. The Planners take all the budgets and use the input, mostly by averaging, to come up with budgets for the following year. After posting their initial budget decisions the Planners consider any more input from members before making the final decision.

From that point on, Managers of ongoing areas or sponsors of special projects which 'pass' in the Trade-Off Game, are responsible for seeing that their areas do not overspend and anyone wanting to take money from an area's budget has to get the agreement of the manager. Individuals can choose to spend their personal allowance as they see fit, either drawing cash, or by ordering things on the daily shopping trips (the shopper then charges the items to the individuals allowance). Use of vehicles, phones, and photocopier are also charged back. If a person overspends their allowance they have some leeway before they need to 'get out of the hole'. A person can be in the allowance hole for up to six months in the previous twelve before incurring any consequences. Someone in the hole for six months in the twelve goes back to being a provisional member, unless they had the foresight to make a contract to work their way out. After six months of provisional membership, if the person is in the black they become a full member again. If they are still owing money, a poll is taken of all full members, on whether to accept or reject the person as a member. If rejected the person must leave the Community. Similar rules apply to people who get behind with work hours and fall in the labour hole. This system allows everyone some slack without leaving the Community wide open to exploitation by someone overspending on themselves.

The Vacation Earnings (VE) system is a regulated exception to income sharing here at Twin Oaks. This is a system where people can take paid work outside the county and keep the money for themselves in a special VE account. The money can be spent on travelling or on consumables, outside the county, but cannot be used on the farm or to buy goods to bring home, which would flaunt the financial inequality in other people's faces. It allows energetic people to use some of their vacation time to fund the rest of their vacation, and since vacation time has to be earned by working the equivalant number of hours over and above the labour quota, the system is self-limiting. For example to have a week's holiday it is necessary to have an extra week's quota of 44 to 47 hours in your vaca-

Reproduced from The Leaves of Twin Oaks

tion balance. This doesn't mean that people having lots of holidays have to do more work in total than other peole do, simply that they fit the year's worth of work into 45 weeks or even 40 weeks. Full details of how the labour credit system works would take too much space, but I'll just briefly say that it's both flexible and humane, with allowances made for sickness, doctors appointments, pregnancy and nursing babies; and includes a progressivly reduced work quota for people aged 50 or more.

If people have special needs and wants for personal spending which they can't afford from their allowance they can apply to the Weeds and Knots committee (Weeds and Knots is a kind of spoonerism for Needs and Wants). The Weeds and Knots budget has a certain amount of money which can be shared each month among suitable applicants. This

Reproduced from The Leaves of Twin Oaks

Pam Dawling *is a dedicated gardener and keen sock-knitter, she was born in 1952, shared a communal house as a student, and lived at Crabapple before moving to Lifespan and then Twin Oaks. She has lived communally for twenty years.*

is another way of 'softening' the personal allowance system.

In these ways Twin Oaks has developed a smooth-running process for sharing income and expenses among 85 members. To achieve this the community has set up clear agreements on responsibilities and rights. The "price" of all this is perhaps somewhere in the realm of having less personal control over our earning and spending. There is less immediate direct personal reward for making extra effort to earn more money (the myth of an individual in mainstream society having a great deal of personal financial control is worth examining, especially in these days of high unemployment and fierce competition for jobs). It may also seem that income pooling generates more paperwork - certainly it does generate some, while eliminating others such as tallies of rent and food costs which are necessary in other communities. For these small costs an income pool of this size gains the practical advantages of sharing a modest amount of money over a large group: bulk-buying, sharing of consumer durables, and the job flexibility which becomes possible. Beyond these practical gains is the deep satisfaction of living in a way which is congruent with political beliefs of co-operation and financial justice, and doing it on a large enough scale to be a valid model to demonstrate the feasibility of these political ideas.

Alternative Communities: the Road to Ecotopia?

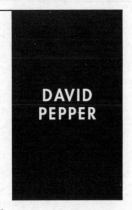

DAVID PEPPER

Many people's dreams of an ecological utopia contain "alternative" communities in them. In some way, communities are often thought to be involved in social change to a green society. However, there are probably more "dreamers" outside the communities than in them - communards themselves are frequently too busy "digging" for their livelihood to spend long in utopian musings.

Academics, like myself, have often theorised about the rôle of communities in two ways. First, they imagine communities as mini-ecotopias in themselves: blueprints of a social formation that will form a large element of the ideal green society of the future. Second, they may think that in the very process of "living it", communards are by-passing conventional capitalist society and therefore weakening and changing it. They are, therefore, achieving a revolution now not by confronting capitalism but by "pre-figuring" what will replace it. Murray Bookchin, Rudolph Bahro, Kirkpatrick Sale, Edward Goldsmith and planner Peter Hall have all contributed to such anarchistic theories.

Before I did some research on them, I also fondly imagined alternative communities as places where, in Marxian terms, unalienated people hunt and fish during the day and plan revolutionary politics until late into the night. However, most communards I talked to rapidly disabused me: they do not see themselves primarily as a revolutionary vanguard, green or otherwise. Indeed, the fundamental barrier preventing the majority of people in the West from living in alternative communities was summed up by someone who has done it for a decade: "... the

When it comes to social change and the movement towards a green society, intentional communities are often perceived as being on the cutting edge. But are they really? Are communards digging so much that they never have any time left in which to dream?

alternative (to conventional life) is too hard - it's boring. You've got to be bred to it through generations. We're too soft. We just can't take it." Another, who has weathered nearly two decades, told me that in living together you do not solve the problems you experience in nuclear families - you merely swap them for another set of equally intractable problems. It's a matter of which set you prefer.

Being Green
Having said that, alternative communities are in theory, and often in practice, green in many ways. For one thing, the politics of communal people are radical - most often anarchist and green, but also socialist or proudly "apolitical" with a strong current of distaste for conventional political parties or approaches.

Their lifestyles strongly feature resource sharing and recycling, home (organic) food production and high food consciousness (vegetarianism, veganism or, most commonly, consuming only products of humanely treated animals). And, often of necessity, they de-emphasise consumerism, pollution, energy use and car transport. What is consumed is thought about - communards are strongly into ethical and environmentally sound lifestyles, and they like the idea of being at one with nature. The whole paraphernalia of deep ecology is conspicuous: holistic medicine, self awareness and - realisation, nature consciousness, therapy and, sometimes, anti-urbanism and anti-industrialism. Many communards attempt, also, to share work and incomes, to achieve participatory (sometimes consensus) democracy, to hear and tolerate most viewpoints, and to work out and reconcile clashes of opinion and personality - either consciously by counselling and therapy or indirectly through everyday working together.

Not that there is unblemished ecological success. Communards may admit to being careless about energy saving and recycling, profligate in car use (especially in the countryside), prone to spending bouts when possible (for instance on cream cake "benders"), liking cigarettes, junk videos and water closets, being lazy about jointly-owned things (leaving tools out), exploiting human labour (particularly their own, by working all hours) and sometimes, best of all, not being guilty about such failings! Most are intelligent enough to realise that guilt about failure to live by high principles is extremely counter-productive. But this pragmatism can lead, however, to a tendency never to discuss principles, high or otherwise.

> in living together you do not solve the problems you experience in nuclear families - you merely swap them for another set of equally intractable problems

Although many individuals regret such an omission, it is an easy way of avoiding recrimination of self or other, and is also easily achieved in the mundane "busyness" of the daily round.

The very intelligence of the inhabitants of alternative communities, together with their extraordinary range of skills and their resourcefulness, constitutes a big reason why contemporary mainstream society would have to change radically before it could be largely made up of such communities. For today's communities are overwhelmingly untypical of the society from which they are drawn. My survey revealed that very many communards have university degrees, are middle-class professionals (or are from such a background) and are mostly drawn from creative, caring or technically skilled occupations. Additionally, they have taught themselves various new skills: the many teachers, for instance, actually become people who can do - farming, gardening, cooking or tractor or car repair for instance.

Revolution or Counter-Revolution

But even if they are to an extent green, this does not mean that alternative communities are exactly making the rest of the world sit up and follow their example. For one thing, the "prefiguring" model of social revolution (which many communards believe in) is seriously flawed, as Marx realised when he attacked utopian socialists and anarchists. By not confronting capitalist power, and not trying to wrest it away from where it is, prefiguring allows the political status quo to thrive - indeed it may even afford a welcome safety valve for capitalism where the socially disaffected can harmlessly let off steam. The model is also idealistic in analysis, holding that the alienated masses will follow the example of the communal vanguard because they see that communities are a good idea. Unfortunately material conditions ensure that this does not happen. By and large today's unemployed do not indulge in positive orgies of building commune-ism: they sink into negativity and inactive despair. And the labour movement, which should be encouraging them to activity, does little about it. Communards, by and large, refuse to work in and on that movement; nor (perhaps wisely) do they any longer have the patience to work in conventional political ways. However, perhaps those in the counterculture who oppose materialism and consumerism should, paradoxically, work for their greater dissemination. For it seems that most people who want to, and do, set up alternative communities have been

> By and large today's unemployed do not indulge in positive orgies of building commune-ism: they sink into negativity and inactive despair.

Circle dancing outside the Universal Hall at Findhorn

....

Failed marriages, loneliness, and inability to afford rising house prices are often the main reasons why people seek a logical way out and live together

....

children of consumerism themselves and have been revolted because they are disaffected with it, not because they cannot achieve it.

Other, more immediate factors, militate against alternative communities as an instrument of social change. Two thirds of those listed in *Diggers and Dreamers* are rural rather than urban, yet it is cities where most of the people who might want radical change live. Many rural communards are uneasy about this. But those who now live in the rural communities which were formed during the first heyday of environmentalism in the early 1970s are not perhaps as uneasy about it as the original communards themselves might have been. For the founders were substantially motivated by green and socialist politics; they did want to change the wider world. Most of these, however, have now gone and with them has gone much of the ideological fervour. The original goals have been displaced (or misplaced). This is partly for practical reasons: as I suggested above, daily existence can be a hard grind of itself, challenging enough, and yet also "safe". And, because many do not stay in communities for long, there has usually in the 1980s and 1990s been a constant need for more people to join. Given the difficulty of getting newcomers, and the importance of their being personally compatible, it is pushing luck then to insist on their political correctness as well. Furthermore, since the 1970s, there have been fewer politically correct people about, wanting to change the world. The new waves of communards have certainly not prioritised building a new green dawn as their motivation for joining. Much more important has been disaffection with conventional society, especially the nuclear family. Failed marriages, loneliness, and inability to afford rising house prices are often the main reasons why people seek a logical way out and live together.

Finally, there is also much evidence to suggest that the "counter culture", of which alternative communities by-and-large are a part, does not stand apart from the mainstream culture it opposes. It is not an independent beacon, shining forth with a steady light of unchanging revolutionary values. Dialectically, its values change, in similar directions, as mainstream values change. There is much evidence to suggest the "Thatcherisation" of alternative communities in the eighties. Privatisation, individualism, consumerism, managerialism, and the values of the market place, of commercial viability and of the nuclear family have all made inroads. Core communal members are not drop-outs today. Some of them "dropped out" in the sixties and seventies (a half of those I surveyed were aged 30 to 39 and a third over 40) and are now busy dropping back in. They are respectable, like their own space, may cook and eat for and by themselves, don't appreciate free-riders or drugs, or "anything goes" anarchism, see the need to balance budgets by earning income, won't or can't draw the dole, and like cars, televisions and compact discs (and who can blame them?)

> Core communal members are not drop-outs today. Some of them "dropped out" in the sixties and seventies and are now busy dropping back in.

In Perspective
If some of this sounds critical about the theory or practice of communities as routes to social change, it is perhaps more a criticism of those who do not live in them rather than those who do. For the former rather than the latter are usually the ones who have unrealistic expectations of such communities. The communards themselves are mainly content to count their blessings in the here and now. These are considerable, and, as I have suggested, they are not irrelevant to a green society.

There is an attempt to throw off mindless consumerism. And there is companionship: some re-appropriation of the communal essence from which we are so often alienated in conventional life. There is, too, a degree of independence and satisfaction in work: albeit often "menial" or mundane. Women particularly seem to value all of these, and additionally they prize the opportunity which alternative communities can offer to break out of gender-rôle stereotypes. They can have a go at a wide range of jobs and develop their slumbering skills; they can show lead-

The Graigians - Green Monks in Kentish Town

David Pepper is Professor of Geography at Oxford Brookes University. He teaches courses on the history of environmental thought and on environmental ideology and politics. He was once a soil surveyor with the Soil Survey of England and Wales. Apart from Communes and the Green Vision (1991), he has written Roots of Modern Environmentalism (1984) and Eco-Socialism:from Deep Ecology to Social Justice (1993).

ership and be respected for it; they can share child-rearing with men and other women; they can be, and are, "breadwinners". This is not to say that patriarchy is absent: neither are other manifestations of the unecological world "outside". But if you are green, there are many worse places to live than a community. You will not get far in one without being realistic. But neither do those who enter their doors have to abandon all hope or idealism.

Developmental Communalism: an alternative approach to Communal Studies

DON PITZER

Communal living is a generic social mechanism available to peoples, governments and movements, past, present, and future. Ancient and modern hunting and gathering peoples and small scale agricultural societies often evidence communal characteristics. Governments place millions of citizens in state sponsored communal projects. Yet communitarian scholarship focuses almost exclusively upon communal usage by religious and secular movements. Leaders of these movements look to communal living as a survival technique, especially during formative stages. They see communes as a means of escaping the old order and seeking a new one either of their own making or produced by divine or historical forces. Communes become laboratories to test and demonstrate new ideologies and systems. For some new movements, communism itself becomes a panacea for world reform. The communes established by movements are small, voluntary social units, partly isolated from the general society, in which members share an ideology, a lifestyle and an economic union while practising their ideal systems. Insistence on inflexibly adhering to communalism and related practises and beliefs can be dysfunctional, however. Movements, as well as governments and peoples, that do not adjust their strictly communal efforts or adopt new organisational forms more suitable to changing internal and external conditions and the needs of rising generations can arrest their own development. At best, they may enter stable states of equilibrium. At worst, they may stagnate and die. Ironically perhaps, the most ardent practitioners of communalism usually witness the decline and death of their larger ideological movements, whereas those who develop beyond

Communal experiments have often been branded failures. This article looks, from a broader perspective, at the part that communes have played in the process of social change. All sorts of movements have adopted communal living in their early stages, abandoning it later, only when it was no longer required.

an early communal phase to more pliable social, economic and administrative forms usually see their causes not only survive but flourish.

Thus, first century Christians adopted communalism to ensure survival, then adapted developmentally providing for the continuation of their religious movement. In both doctrine and community of goods, early Christianity adjusted and made possible the expansion of the faith to Gentiles. Biblical evidence suggests that Paul may have developed the doctrine of justification by faith to solve the communal problem of assimilating non-Jewish converts into the Christian community without circumcision or compliance with Jewish dietary regulations. Growth of the Christian movement ultimately took precedence over communal living and legalistic enforcement of Hebrew law upon Gentile Christians. The developmental approach prevailed, and the vitality of Christianity resulted.

Christian communalism nevertheless continued having an influence as the principal communal model for religious movements in the Western World. Many of these, such as the Seventh-Day Baptists and Mormons, developed beyond an early communal phase, like Christianity itself. However, less developmentally adaptive religious sects suffered the fate of the now moribund Shakers. The Amish and Hutterites stand as exceptions, maintaining their communities over centuries by unique adaptations.

The non-sectarian reform movements inspired by Robert Owen of New Lanark, and Charles Fourier of Paris lived past their ephemeral communal stages to realise many of their reform goals through other means. Today, the maturing Kibbutz movement in Israel and the aging membership of the Roman Catholic Religious Orders in America grapple with their own developmental challenges. Their respective abilities at innovative adaptation will determine the future of the causes.

The foregoing historical facts and assumptions suggest the process and approach of "developmental communalism". Developmental communalism is the process of adopting communal living and collective economies as useful, perhaps essential, arrangements during a formative stage of social, political, religious or reform development and of altering or abandoning communal forms, economies, and practices in response to subsequent challenges and needs. The approach of developmental communalism takes into account the tendency of peoples, their governments and their movements to become communal, the variety of practices and ideologies employed while living communally, and the necessary changes made in communal efforts to objectives while avoiding collective stagnation, boredom and, possibly, death.

The Developmental Approach

Developmental communalism recognises three essential facts about communal living and collective economies. First, they are universally available to peoples, governments and movements. Second, communal practices are often adopted out of necessity for security, stability and survival during the emergence of a people, a culture, a political programme or a religious or secular movement. Third, and possibly most important, that communal usage is sometimes altered creatively or abandoned altogether for more relevant organisational strategies as new circumstances and opportunities arise, both preserving and perhaps invigorating the original culture, government or movement and its long term objectives.

Developmental communalism therefore encourages a shift in the focus of scholarly attention from the internal factors that produce or inhibit survival of the communal structure itself to a consideration of the entire history and influence of the movements of which communalism is a single facet. We can examine the origins, objectives and achievements of entire movements. We can begin to put the communal phase into its proper place and can sense its true function. We can look with greater specificity at subtle changes in communal practices made to preserve movements themselves. We can isolate the factors and conditions that identify the groups which adopt to change most effectively. We can gain new appreciation for the movements which have developed beyond their communal stages to solve the divisive problems caused by the influx of new members or the coming of new generations and intense ideological imperatives that drove the original members to the disciplines and sacrifices, as well as the psychological, social and economic support of intentional community.

••••••••••••••••••••

communal practices are often adopted out of necessity for security, stability and survival during the emergence of a people, a culture, a political programme or a religious or secular movement

••••••••••••••••••••

The Development Approach In Practice

The universal appeal of communal methods and the variety of their application are discovered in the customs of sharing food and other resources embedded in many hunting, gathering, pastoral and horticultural societies of the past and present. In these groups sharing and survival are inseparable. Selfishness and hoarding are intolerable. Rights to use communal resources preclude private ownership of property except for small personal items. Theoretically, everyone owns a share in virtually everything claimed by the band, the kinship group, the tribe. However, sharing occurs under carefully prescribed conditions that do not necessarily permit equal shares on any given occasion. Communalism of this type is best compared to the reciprocity in food, favours and labour occurring in families of all ages and places.

Governments, especially new regimes and their agents, use communal methods to pacify conquered peoples, settle new territories, solidify domestic control and solve economic problems. The Spanish and Portuguese governments authorised the mission village system as a means of Indian pacification in the Western Hemisphere. Their agents were the regular clergy of the Roman Catholic Religious Orders. Of particular interest are the villages created in sixteenth century New Spain by Franciscan Vasco de Quiroga. His Indian villages are modelled after Thomas More's Utopia, complete with community of property and labour, and representative government.

Beginning in 1910, socialist Zionists created Kibbutzim as communally-organised units of occupation which helped make possible the establishment of the state of Israel in 1948. Since then, the Israeli government has given land and other assistance to the kibbutzim as centres for civil defence and economic development. Having realised most of its original nationalistic goals, the socialistic Zionist movement has formed 269 efficient, effective, thoroughly communal kibbutzim. In the decades since 1910, the movement has made many organisational adjustments and now faces the ultimate developmental challenge. For many kibbutzniks, the desire to continue the discipline of communal living is no longer strong or driven by the necessities and ideology of the early movement. Kibbutz population may be on the decline as fewer than 60% of the children raised in kibbutzim choose to apply for life membership. The materialism of the

....
For many kibbutzniks, the desire to continue the discipline of communal living is no longer strong or driven by the necessities and ideology of the early movement.
....

general society shows in suggestions of five day working weeks, bonuses for overtime, and more luxury items in the kibbutz. Some want fewer roles and abandonment of the central dining room which has typified communal life. These important indicators are not lost on kibbutz leaders who, by addressing them in open forums, demonstrate the signs of concern and vitality in the larger movement. Major adjustments in kibbutz

A group pf Shaker communards in 1875

form and practice continually take place. In April 1987, the Kibbutz Artzi, a federation of some 80 kibbutzim, decided formally to sanction the growing practice of housing children with their parents, a significant trend away from the more economical and co-operative childcare centres established by the founders.

In an early phase of new political regimes and during economic, social or political crises the Soviet Union, United States, China and other nations resorted to the apparent benefits of communal programmes. Stalin came to power in 1924 and initiated collective farms in the Soviet Union four years later. The United States in the Roosevelt New Deal period set up 100 subsistence Homesteads, aiding the unemployed through the Department of Agriculture's Farm Security Administration. In 1958 Mao Zedong undertook the largest communal project in history, ultimately putting 800 million Chinese into People's Communes as part of his 'Great Leap Forward' campaign. Because of languishing production due to loss of worker incentive, the Chinese government began to dismantle its People's Communes in 1982. For the same reason, Gorbachev's peristroika of the Soviet economy attempted to stimu-

late the collective farmers by offering land and stock.

Developmentally speaking, here again we can witness political movements pursuing survival by both adopting communalism and by changing or rejecting communal projects over time to sustain the larger governmental objectives.

A view of the Shaker Community at Church Family, Hancock, Massachusetts showing the meetinghouse, shops, large communal dwelling, and round barn with conical roof

The Developmental Approach to Traditional Communalism

Finally, and perhaps most significantly, the concept of developmental communalism broadens the horizons for study of the religious and secular movements which traditionally have occupied the centre stage of communal scholarship. From a developmental approach, a communal society can only be defined as a social structure employed during a period of time by those practising and promoting a particular ideology or system. In this view the use of communalism by any movement, even if over many years and justified by divine fiat, is an expedient not to be confused with the movement itself. Therefore, the term communal society assumes new meaning, or simply becomes moot.

The same is true for the vague and confusing use of the phrase 'communal movement' to suggest that many communes are being created by various groups and causes during certain historic periods. Sometimes these groups and causes have the avowed purpose of escaping society, sometimes of saving the world through "patent-office models of the good society" or through "intentional communities". However, upon close examination it becomes evident that the communes of the so-called 'communal movement' were instituted by people from many different religions and ideological persuasions with little or no direct connection to each other. In some instances the various causes disagree with, and even oppose, each other while drawing upon the same generic communal reservoir as a convenient, often idealised, source for surviving and realising their objectives. In reality, general, unified communal movements are a fiction. The expansive use of communal living in recent years, like past communal movement mirages, resolves itself upon closer inspection into numerous smaller ideological causes having adopted communalism for their own reasons as suggested by developmental communalism. And once again communal living becomes a vehicle rather than a destination. Furthermore, to those individual contemporary movements planning to make communal living an end in itself as the centrepiece for reforming the world or any significant segment thereof, developmental theory speaks a sharp warning: no movement has succeeded in any such scheme. As insulated, self-selected social laboratories, communal societies apparently are impotent for effecting such universal reform.

Developmental Communalism and Communal Studies

The developmental approach could liberate scholarship in communal studies from the stereotypes and intellectual cul-de-sacs implied by our past reliance upon the concepts of 'communal societies' and 'communal movements', of 'success' and 'failure'. It could produce new understandings. We might learn, for example, the critical decisions relative to communalism which sealed the fates of movements; decisions made by the Harmonists in the 1810s, Zoarites in the 1820s, Shakers in the 1830s and Oneidans in the 1870s. We might discover reasons why the Moravians developed beyond their purely communal ways in the 1760s and 70s, the Mormons in the 1840s, and the hippies of The Farm in Tennessee in the 1980s. Further, we might see clearly for the first time that movements which consistently have been labelled "unsuccessful" from the older 'success-failure' interpretation may now be seen to have passed through a communal stage only to achieve many of their objectives in other structures and by other means. Owenism is only one movement which will appear differently from this developmental viewpoint.

Many used the expression "afterglow" in describing the achievements of the Owenites at New Harmony after the Owen-Maclure-Fretageot community was dissolved in 1827. From a developmental perspective we can amplify this impression with examples of the influence of Owen, his ideas and his followers in the United States, Britain and around the world from the 1820s to the present. They include 160 working men's libraries funded in Indiana and Illinois by Robert Owen's Scottish partner, William Maclure; feminism, birth control and emancipation of American slaves were championed

[1] **KANTER, R M** (1972) *Commitment and Community* Harvard University Press, Cambridge, Mass.

by Frances Wright and Owen's eldest son, Robert Dale; property rights for Indiana women and tuition-free schools for Indiana boys and girls were pieces of legislation which Robert Dale Owen helped achieve while a member of the Indiana General Assembly. In Britain Owen's own lifelong reform efforts before and after his American communal venture earned him a worldwide reputation related to efficient industrial management, improved living and cultural standards for the working classes, early socialism and feminism, progressive education, the modern co-operative movement and trade unionism.

Evidence such as this strongly suggests that while the Owenite efforts at community building were short-lived, ill-managed and, possibly, ill-advised, the Owenite movement was not, to use Kanter's term, 'unsuccessful'.[1] Using developmental communalism we can put Owenism and other movements and their communal stages in more realistic perspective.

Conclusion

In conclusion, developmental communalism invites us to consider a new approach to communal studies, to try a new paradigm, to reach new understandings. If we accept the invitation we will view communal living as a generic social mechanism available to peoples, governments and movements, past, present and future. We will expand our investigations into bands, kinship groups, tribal societies and communal government projects in addition to our traditional focus on the communes of religious and secular movements. We will analyse movements themselves in their totalities as well as in their communal phases. Therefore, we will reach beyond the simplistic 'success-failure' approach based on communal longevity and evaluate entire movements based on their goals and achievements. Through our developmental interpretation of communal experience we will help place all communes in more accurate perspective.

Dr Donald Pitzer chairs the History Department and directs the Center for Communal Studies at the University of Southern Indiana and is executive director of the Communal Studies Association. He is editing an anthology based on developmental communalism theory.

Towards a Green Society: Can the creation of new communities still play a part?

ANDY
WOOD

In this article I shall argue that whilst alternative communities have lost their revolutionary zeal (if they ever had any), new kinds of intentional communities, of a non-utopian type, may still be what the Green movement needs.

I shall begin, with the help of Andrew Dobson's analysis in *Green Political Thought*, by summarising the current position of the Green movement. Then, borrowing Don Pitzer's concept of "Developmental Communalism", I suggest that the past 25 years could pre-figure a radical Green political movement. Finally, by looking at some current communal and community developments, I suggest that these are still important to the progress of such a movement.

Current Green Politics

The position of the Green movement as a political force is uncertain. In his book, *Green Political Thought*[1], Andrew Dobson argues that it stands at a crossroads between being absorbed into liberal reformist politics and evolving into a radical political force by becoming the focus of oppositional belief and action for subordinate groups in society. The majority of Greens are, according to Dobson, reformists - what Jonathon Porrit calls 'light' greens. Their approach to the ecological question is environmental management within the context of present political and economic practices.

Radical or 'dark' Greens assume, however, that the current industrial-capitalist system is inimical to a Green, sustainable society. Dobson suggests that the 'dark green' position is emerging as a new political ideology, which he calls "ecologism", because it contains both a critique of the existing system as a

If communes are unlikely spearheads of fundamental social change (Pepper), but can be seen as part of a process from which new political movements might emerge (Pitzer), do alternative communities still have any part to play in creating a Green society?

whole, and a vision of a fundamentally different one, the sustainable society. The radical Green position pre-supposes therefore that society should undergo fundamental transformation. If we accept this premise, then what are the best strategies to adopt to transform society into a Green sustainable one? There has been "very little serious thinking" on this question, according to Dobson.

Common Ground in Birmingham is more than just a housing co-op. It's members are involved a whole network of activities in the local urban area.

Dobson assesses existing Green strategies: parliamentary activity through new Green parties, greening conventional parties, and pressure group activity; lifestyle changes through consumer habits; and 'small experimental' communities in ecological living. At best these will, he concludes, result in environmental reforms, not fundamental social transformations. Dobson says that before we can really get to grips with how to create more fundamental changes, radical Greens have first to tackle the question of who is most likely to achieve it.

Apart from a few morally or educationally enlightened people who can think globally and long term, the concepts of ecologism are remote from the everyday lives of most people. This is because anywhere and at any time most people are "concerned with matters that affect only family and friends over a short period of time". If ecologism is to become relevant to these people, then it needs to go further than appealing to their 'higher consciences' and address the everyday conditions in which they work and live. To develop into a political force ecologism has to appeal to people "whose immediate interests lie in living a green life" (p 154). A possible strategy for the Green movement, says Dobson, is "... to identify

[1]DOBSON, A (1990) *Green Political Thought* Routledge, London

and foment a group in society that is not only relatively 'disengaged' from it, but that also is already inclined towards the foundations of sustainable living." (page 162) Such a group might include the long-term unemployed, the retired, and women and children[2]. These people could be made aware that the cycle of production and consumption has no future for them and that their "... interests lie in a different form of society rather than immersion in the present one"(p 168).

But how can the Green movement make such a group aware that their interests lie in a sustainable system rather than a capitalist-consumer one? Disengaged they might be, but they are not likely to be inclined towards sustainable living unless the cultural attachments to consumer society have been undone. Those who are already 'disengaged' and also inclined towards a sustainable lifestyle, tend to be those who have voluntarily abandoned the materialist ethic which consumer society depends on, and begun pioneering alternative lifestyles. Whilst the 'small experimental' utopian community is rightly seen as a naïve attempt to bring change through the 'force of example', we still need some kind of consciousness-raising mechanism.

Development of Communalism and the Green Movement

As a vehicle for achieving fundamental social change, utopian communalism commands a more than usual level of support amongst dissenting groups at times when existing political ideologies and movements are not relevant to their cause, and before new ones have emerged.[3] Communalism, according to Don Pitzer's ideas on Developmental Communalism (see previous article), can be regarded as a necessary, even essential, set of organisational arrangements in the formative stage in the development of a new political movement. Historical examples include the millenialist communities in the late Middle Ages which preceeded Protestantism and the Reformation; and the utopian socialist communities which preceeded Marxism and subsquent communist revolutions. In the 1960s a new generation of utopian communities sprang up: people 'dropped out' and experiments in ecological living abounded.

Many communards in the 1960s and 1970s believed that their example could revolutionise society. David Pepper (see earlier article) has explained the process by which such revolutionary fervour is

....

Whilst the 'small experimental' utopian community is rightly seen as a naïve attempt to bring change through the 'force of example', we still need some kind of consciousness-raising mechanism.

....

[2]Dobson posits a Green materialist analysis (see pp 162-9) whereby material shortages (and pollution prevention costs) force a reduction in other production costs, and encourage increased consumption in order to generate more investment capital. As a result specific social groups could get squeezed completely out of the production/consumption system.

[3]see **WOOD, A** (1991) *The Third Garden City* unpublished Open University thesis, pp 7-9

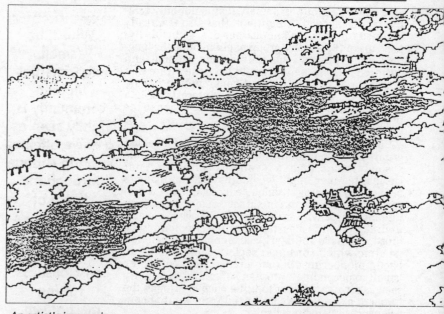

An artist's impression of the proposed Stroud Sustainable Village. The whole project is a long way in conception from the 'all or nothing' communes of the 1960s and 70s.

neutralised and such groups assimilated back into the system they initially set out to change and escape.[4]

This should come as no surprise because the utopian community is not a viable strategy of revolution for three reasons. The utopian community is essentially an attempt to create a model of a new society. Internal and external pressures to make it impractical, however, to perfect. Secondly it is ineffectual to try and provoke political and social action only by appealing to people's consciences without also addressing their everyday material conditions. Finally, the utopian community has always had a secondary function for many participants: to provide an escape or sanctuary. Communities often become conservative rather than embark on activities in the outside world which might threaten or destabilise them.

Instead, Developmental Communalism explains their function as a symbol of the new ecological consciousness: a means of fomenting and launching ecological ideals and social and political objectives. Only history will tell if these 'alternative' communities portend the development of a radical Green

[4]see also **PEPPER, D** (1991) *Communes and the Green Vision* Green Print, London

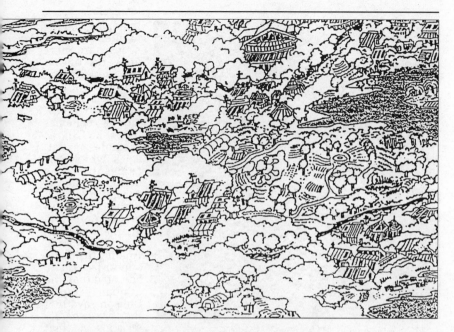

movement. Communal groups still exist and are still being formed however. Does it mean that the Green movement still needs utopian communities?[5] There might be one or two projects around still trying to escape the system and create models to convert the world to ecologism by force of their example. But most communal groups are formed because many people simply find it an expedient and pleasant domesticity; preferable to the conventional alternatives of living alone or in nuclear families, whilst still 'living lightly upon the Earth'.

So communal groups are, by and large, no longer utopian: no longer escapes from society as safe havens for their inhabitants, departing from society to seek the perfect human existence and attempting to create a model example of the ecological society. They might still be worthwhile alternative homes, even to the extent of aiding the active, committed Green radical. Does it mean that new community building *per se* is valueless in terms of effective strategies for Green change?

Both Dobson and Pepper are more optimistic about a new type of intentional community which instead of being geographically integral and socially inward-

[5] It should be noted, that many communal groups were never utopian in this sense. Abrams and McCulloch's study (see 'Useful Books') makes clear that three other different types of communal group existed. For further discussion see 'History and Overview' in **ANSELL, V et al (ed)** (1989) *Diggers and Dreamers: The 1990/91 Guide to Communal Living* Communes Network, Sheffield.

The housing co-ops in and around Milton Keynes are trying to forge closer links. The photograph shows a network bar-b-que held at Redfield Community.

looking - like the utopian communities - are more networks of living, working and commodity exchange. Dobson refers to local money schemes (like LETS) as examples of strategies which circumvent the existing producer/consumer system. Pepper refers to this as a possible alternative political economy. Arguing that these appear less easily co-opted than the utopian types, Dobson says that they have characteristics "that might well qualify them as a part-strategy for the possible agents of change ..."(page 152)

Sustainable Living Systems

A LETS (Local Exchange Trading System) is a system for organising skill sharing using local currency. LETS systems have caused a good deal of interest internationally in the Green movement with over 45 now in operation in the UK. Another new idea was put forward by How and Poulter in *Diggers and Dreamers 92/93*, for new communities emerging as 'anchor points' in, what they called, 'sustainable living systems':

> *"A sustainable living system will link together a whole range of different progressive organisations which involve some aspect of co-operation but at many differing levels and types of location. It could include anything from a shared household to a community enterprise; from a food co-op run by neighbours to a housing co-op where everyone has their own house; from an urban worker co-op to the archetypal commune in the nearby countryside."*[6]

> *"The main difference between New Communities and the ... (utopian) models will be the way in which they will relate to the wider world. Instead of seeing it as something 'out there' to be protected and disconnected from, New*

[6] How, J and Poulter, S in **COATES, C et al (ed)** (1991) *Diggers and Dreamers 92/93* Communes Network, Milton Keynes

Communities will engage with society and make a conscious effort to pull the 'reality' of the world towards a new 'vision'.[7]

[7]*ibid* pp 25-6

How and Poulter's new communities would be communal groups much like the ones which exist already, but more stable and outward-looking because they would be integrated into a whole network of similar organisations, which will also contribute to making the whole network more politically effective. But the sustainable living systems themselves are also a new type of community: geographically spread throughout an area, linked functionally rather than being integrally and spatially contiguous. Around the country there is some indication that networks of "Alternative Lifestylers" exist. There are particular areas renowned for them (eg Totnes and Glastonbury) but through the grapevine one hears about other examples, and perhaps each locality already has its own embryonic network. Are these potential 'sustainable living systems'?

Whilst How and Poulter are advocating their new breed of intentional communities, they make reference to changes taking place in existing ones. There is a trend away from the socially insular, geographically integral community. They give Laurieston Hall and Findhorn as examples of communities which are becoming less communal but appear to be functionally spreading out into the surrounding neighbourhood. Whilst Pepper argues that these have been assimilated more than most back into the system, if we apply Pitzer's developmental explanation, perhaps these too are potential 'sustainable living systems'.

Conclusion

Green philosophers have a tendency to think that a sustainable society will be structured around self-contained communities, but will community building play a role in that society? If utopian communities are, as Pitzer's theory suggests, a necessary early stage in the development of a new political movement (rather than, as Pepper suggests, naïve diversions from it) what does the future hold, both for intentional communities and the Green movement?

I do not think that there are any answers to these questions right now. But I do believe that they underlie the most pressing question which radical Greens currently face, which is: what strategies are likely to

[8]LANDRY et al quoted in PEPPER, p 214

bring fundamental changes? What is alarming is that it is a question that the movement does not appear to be addressing. In the absence of such debate, the idea of networks of sustainable living groups and communities is at least a welcome beginning.

Whether one is looking at emerging new communities; the developments within existing ones; or plans for local money schemes; then some kind of yardstick is required to assess their potential as an effective strategy for change. Landry *et al* offer us some guidance on what characteristics to look for:

"... it should first and foremost be an economic network - as near as possible to an 'alternative political economy', capable of sustaining itself:

a *by inter-action with 'the sea of capitalism' in which it is set*

b *by economic interchange between the network's members*

c *by such interchange with other elements of an alternative economy ..."*[8]

The advantage of local money schemes is that as trade within the scheme increases, the scheme becomes less vulnerable and dependent on inter-action with the capitalist system. The disadvantage is that the sustainable living system might come to be seen as the goal itself, rather than as part of the political struggle to achieve the Green sustainable society.

As the 20th Century draws to a close, the way the Green movement develops will play a significant role in shaping society in the next. Whatever direction it takes, it would seem possible that new communities could play a part. The question remains, what type of community and how great a part?

Andy Wood is a part time Geography tutor with the University of Westminster and the Open University. He also works occasionally for the Milton Keynes Environmental Network and the Co-operatives Research Unit. He is dad to Rosie, who lives with him during the school week at their house in Rainbow Housing Co-operative.

1994/95 Directory of Communities

Living together, sharing resources, creating new structures for ourselves, the groups listed in this directory potentially offer an alternative to the isolation, wastefulness and disempowerment of much of modern life. Some of these groups may work together, some may income share, some may have a spiritual focus, some may not necessarily live under the same roof; whole groups or people within the groups may be committed to ideals such as permaculture, veganism, home education and struggling against sexism, racism and homophobia; others may well not.

Please bear in mind that there are many other communal groups who are not listed, including countless urban house-shares, but all the groups in this directory share a desire to be public about their lifestyle; many are looking for new members, and most of them welcome visitors. If you are thinking of setting up a new group, or joining an existing one, this is the place to start. If you are planning to visit one of these groups for the first time, it is well worth reading our section 'How to Visit a Community'. Whatever you do, please don't just turn up. Remember that you will be going into people's homes, and it is important to write to them and wait for an invitation to come. You will find that some groups set aside particular times for welcoming first-time visitors. Yet again some of these communities host a whole range of workshops, courses and working weekends and you may find these a good way of visiting for the first time, although you probably won't get a flavour of day-to-day communal life. Don't be shy of visiting, though; most groups rely on

This section contains 88 entries from communal groups which are either already established or are on their way to being so. To help you locate the communities that interest you there is a quick reference index and a map.

a stream of visitors to find the new members that are essential for the life of the community.

How to use the Index, Map and Directory

The Index details seven features which help distinguish different types of groups. This is not meant to be a 'scientifically sound' classification, but should help when selecting the groups you may wish to visit. We have gone, as far as possible, by groups' own answers to the questions.

A ■ is only shown in the Income sharing?, Capital needed? and Communal meals? columns if their answer was definitely "yes". If their answer was "no" or ambiguous then nothing is shown. In those cases it might mean, for example, that they do income share in some way or that they do eat communally occasionally. Where a group's diet is shown as vegetarian (vtn) it means that they never, ever consume any meat; and where it is vegan (vgn) that they never, ever consume any animal products.

A letter denotes those communities with a spiritual focus:

A   Anthroposophy (the philosophy of Steiner)
B   Buddhist
C   Christian
H   Hindu
Q   Quaker
S   Spiritual but non specific

The numbers on both the index and the map refer to the number given to each group in the 'Directory', not to its page number in the book. Some communities did not wish to be shown on the map, for some embryonic groups it was also inappropriate. Entries are ordered alphabetically. Where a community has a link with other communities of the same generic type or its philosophy is included in its name, its geographical location is given first followed by the generic name/philosophy. This may not necessarily be the "official" name of the community (eg Botton Camphill is a Camphill community located at Botton in Yorkshire, its "official" name is Botton Village).

Embryonic communities are included in the Index and are shown in italics in order to distinguish them from existing communities. It is clearly not possible for them to give an answer to all the questions. Where answers are given they are likely to be aspirations rather than actualities. Some networks of communities have a single entry for the entire network. Sometimes they have provided meaningful figures for numbers, sometimes it has not been possible.

As you will see, some groups have a very clear Ideological focus whereas others have found it impossible to answer this question and have left that part of their entry blank. The question Open to new members? is a general one. A group that is closed indefinitely will answer "no". However a group which is open in principal to new members (and therefore answers "yes") may not necessarilly have any spaces at the time at which you contact them.

PhONE Day

On April 16 1995 all UK area codes starting with "0" will change so that they start "01". Birmingham's codes, for example, will change from 021 to 0121; Charmouth from 0297 to 01297. In addition, each of the following cities will be allocated a new area code:

Leeds 0532 xxxxxx becomes 0113 2xx xxxx

Sheffield 0742 xxxxxx becomes 0114 2xx xxxx

Nottingham 0602 xxxxxx becomes 0115 9xx xxxx

Leicester 0533 xxxxxx becomes 0116 2xx xxxx

Bristol 0272 xxxxxx becomes 0117 9xx xxxx

The old numbers are shown in the Directory but any telephone numbers for the five above-mentioned cities are followed by ⬛! to remind you of the substantial change in the dialling code.

Disclaimer

Reading through the directory you may decide that some entries push the boundaries of communalism somewhat. The editorial team decided that it should be for the groups themselves to decide whether they should be included. We must point out that we cannot take responsibility for the accuracy of entries, as we are not in a position to verify information sent to us, nor can we be held responsible for anything that may occur to individuals visiting groups as result of reading this directory. Good luck!

Apology

In Diggers and Dreamers 92/93, *as entry 73 in the Directory of Communities, we inadvertently published misleading information as to the number of people involved in* Some People in Leicester. *We accept that to talk of numbers made no sense of their co-operative network. The editorial team unreservedly apologise for this mistake.*

Name	Code number	Situation	Number of over 18s	Number of under 18s	Income sharing?	Capital required?	Communal meals?	Diet	Spiritual focus?
The Abbey	1	village	6	0			■	vtn	C
Argyle Street	2	urban	87	9					
Ashram	3	urban	5	0			■		C
Balnakeil	4	rural	26	17		■			
Beech Hill	5	rural	20	6					
Beeston House	6	suburban	6	0			■	vtn	C
Bhaktivedanta	7	rural	150	40			■	vtn	H
Birchwood Hall	8	rural	12	2			■		
Blackcurrent	9	urban	5	2			■	vgn	
Botton Camphill	10	rural	260	50	■		■		A
Brambles/Magic	11	urban	4	2	■		■	vgn	
Braziers	12	rural	15	0			■		
Cambridge Buddhist	13	urban	35	0			■	vgn	B
Canon Frome	14	rural	29	25		■			
Centre for Alt Tech	15	rural	12	3			■		
Centre for Hol Living	16	*semi-rural*	10				■	*vtn*	
Common Ground	17	urban	22	3				vgn	
E Lancs/Burnleywood	18	urban	7	7					
E Lancs/PiC	18	semi-rural	5	3					
E Lancs/New Comm	18	*semi-rural*							
l'Arche	19	network	150	4			■		C
Community Creation	20	*urban*							
St Clare	21	rural	14	0	■		■		C
Crabapple	22	rural	7	4	■		■		
Darvell Bruderhof	23	rural	140	140	■		■		C
Earthworm	24	rural	8	4	■		■	vgn	
Isle of Erraid	25	rural	9	4			■	vtn	S
Family Tree	26	urban	8	0			■	vtn	C
The Family	27	network			■		■		C
Findhorn Foundation	28	urb & rur	130	22			■		S
Gaunts House	29	rural	25	6			■	vtn	
Giroscope	30	*urban*							
Glaneirw	31	rural	7	3	■		■		
Glencraig Camphill	32	rural			■		■		A
Graigian Society	33	urban	3	0	■		■	vtn	S
Grail Society	34	suburban	24		■		■		C
Grimstone	35	rural	7	3		■	■		S
Gwerin	36	urban	20	6			■		
Harmony	37								
Hengrave Hall	38	rural	20	0			■		C
Iona	39	rural					■		C
Keveral Farm	40	rural	10	3			■		
Laurels	41	urban	8	4					
Laurieston Hall	42	rural	24	8					
Lifespan	43	moorland	8	4	■		■	vtn	

Name	Code number	Situation	Number of over 18s	Number of under 18s	Income sharing?	Capital required?	Communal meals?	Diet	Spiritual focus?
Little Grove	44	rural	14	0		■	■		
Lothlorien	45	rural	14	0			■		
Lower Shaw Farm	46	urban	6	7			■		
Mickleton Emmisary	47	village	45	9			■		S
Monimail Tower	48	rural	11	0			■		
Monkton Wyld	49	rural	15	7			■	vtn	
Mornington Grove	50	urban	12	2				vtn	
New Creation	51	network	550	250	■		■		C
Newbold House	52	rural	7	0			■	vtn	S
Ochil Tower	53	rural	25	35			■		A
Old Hall	54	rural	41	17		■			
Parsonage Farm	55	rural	9	5			■		
Pennine Camphill	56	semi-rural	55	19	■		■		A
Peoples Land Group	57		30						
Plants for a Future	58	rural	5	0				vgn	
Post Green	59	rural	15	4					C
Postlip Hall	60	rural	16	13		■			
Quaker, Bamford	61	rural	15	5					Q
Quaker Comm Project	62								Q
Radical Routes	63	network							
Rainbow	64	urban	27	19					
Redfield	65	rural	15	10			■		
Ritherdon Road	66	urban	7	0			■	vtn	
Rivendell	67	rural	6	0			■		C
Salisbury Centre	68	urban	6	0			■	vtn	S
Sarana	69	urban	7	0			■	vtn	B
Scargill House	70	rural	39+	2			■		C
Sheiling Camphill	71	rural	160	90			■		A
Shrubb Family	72	rural	6	4			■		
Simon	73	urb & rur	45	0			■		
Solaris	74	urban	70						
Some Friends	75	urban	14	2			■		Q
Some People	76	urban	15	7					
Spiritual Family	77	urban	4	1					S
Stroud Sust Village	78								
Summerhill	79	urban	14	0			■	vtn	
T H A T Community	80	urban	30	10			■		
Taena	81	rural	15	7				Vtn	C
Talamh	82	rural	5	0	■		■		
Taraloka	83	rural	8	0			■	vtn	B
Tipi Village	84	rural	80	40					S
Two Mules	85	urban	4	2			■	vgn	
Vegan Housing Coll	86	urban						vgn	
Whitbourne Hall	87	rural	20	25		■			
Wild Lavender	88	urban	6	0			■	vtn	

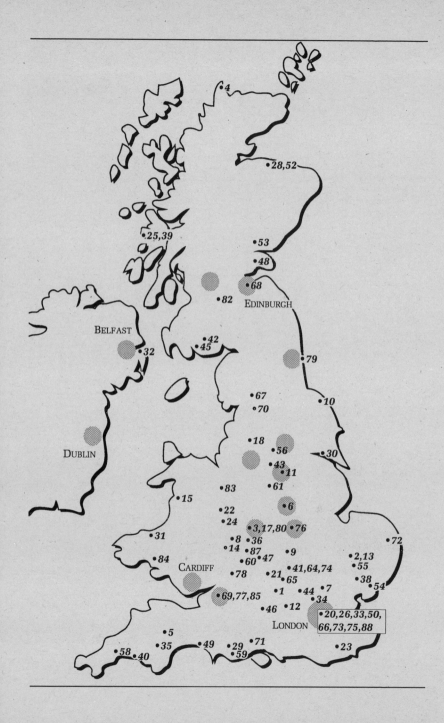

- 4

- 28,52

- 25,39

- 53
- 48
- 68
- 82
EDINBURGH

BELFAST
- 32

- 42
- 45

- 79

- 67
- 70

- 10

DUBLIN

- 18
- 56
- 43
- 11
- 30

- 83
- 61

- 15

- 6

- 22
- 24
- 3,17,80
- 76

- 31

- 8
- 36
- 14
- 87
- 60
- 47
- 9

- 72

- 2,13
- 55

- 84

CARDIFF

- 78
- 21
- 41,64,74
- 65

- 38
- 54

- 1
- 44
- 7
- 34

- 69,77,85

- 46
- 12

- 20,26,33,50,
66,73,75,88
LONDON

- 5
- 35
- 49
- 29
- 71
- 59
- 23

- 58
- 40

R ooted in the Christian tradition, yet open to the wisdom of other faiths and to the challenge of the modern world. The Abbey Sutton Courtenay is a Community and a Conference/Retreat Centre, recognising the sacred dimensions in all areas of life. The Community consists of both resident and non-resident members carrying forward the vision of its founders "to re-discover Christ" in the context of today's modern society. It's everyday life is based on what it perceives as the four right relationships: to God, to the Earth, to ourselves and to others.

The Abbey's programme provides the opportunity to explore each of these relationships through retreats, inter-faith dialogue, healing work and day and weekend courses, focusing on such subjects as ecology, alternative economics and politics, the arts, non-violence and energy. The small resident community attempts to live out these four right relationships by living together co-operatively, simply and ecologically, and by sharing regular time for meditation and worship.

The community also cares for a large and historically .interesting fourteenth century house with rooms available to other groups and a library which includes most of Gandhi's published works. There are four acres of grounds, including a walled organic vegetable garden and a guest annexe which accommodates up to 14. The resident community meets regularly with members of the Council of Management to ensure the smooth running of both business and human aspects of the Abbey, and well as forwarding the vision of its founders, and late Fred J Blum and the, now retired, Bishop Stephen Verney.

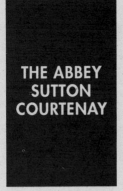

THE ABBEY SUTTON COURTENAY

1

THE GUIDE TO COMMUNAL **LIVING**
DIGGERS & DREAMERS
94/95

Status
existing community

Address
The Green
Sutton Courtenay
ABINGDON
Oxfordshire
OX14 4AF

Telephone
0235 847401

Number of over 18s
6

Number of under 18s
0

Year started
1979

Situation
village

Ideological focus
mixed

Open to new members
Yes

THE GUIDE TO
COMMUNAL
LIVING
DIGGERS &
DREAMERS
94/95

2

Status
existing community

Address
3 Fletchers Terrace
CAMBRIDGE
CB1 3LU

Telephone
0223 411615

Number of over 18s
87

Number of under 18s
9

Year started
1981

Situation
urban

Ideological focus
co-operation

Open to new members
Yes

Argyle Street Housing Co-operative opened in 1981 to cater for 96 young single people in housing need. As a "fully mutual" housing co-operative, all tenants are members of the Co-op, and all members are tenants. While initial funding came from the Housing Corporation, day-to-day finances (to ensure that the Co-op, as a community, its gardens, office, meeting room and 23 houses all stay together at their seams) are provided by modest rent charges.

Home to diverse philosophies, decisions on how the Co-op is run are taken at monthly general meetings of Co-op members in the community "Hut". A number of smaller groups ensure that vacancies are filled, houses and grounds are maintained, that training needs are met and that rent is collected, assisted by the full-time administrative worker.

The Co-op is in an urban environment, close to the railway and consists of 13 shared houses for four, six and ten people, with 10 self-contained, one-bedroom flats which are allocated to housing single parents. Members in the shared houses have individual tenancies for their rooms, sharing kitchens, bathrooms, toilets, showers, sitting rooms and their own level of communal living, while all share communal gardens and an allotment on our three acre site.

With vacancies occuring fairly frequently, applications are always welcome from self-motivated people who are keen to be part of the fun and frustrations of running their own housing and living co-operatively. Contact the Allocations Group.

W e are an intentional Christian community in Inner City Birmingham. We are trying to live out the challenges of radical Christian discipleship. For us this means:

- living among people that have been marginalised, economically and/or socially, by British society
- pooling our resources of time, energy, skills and money in order to respond to needs within our neighbourhood
- running our house as a place of welcome for a wide variety of people; bridge building between people of different cultures, faiths and walks of life
- opening our door to people in crisis, any time of day or night
- actively participating in the life of the neighbourhood
- eating, working, discussing, celebrating and worshipping together
- committing ourselves to each other; supporting and challenging in honest relationships
- working for social justice, sharing particular concern for this with Black minority groups living in this city
- working with people with learning difficulties.

ASHRAM COMMUNITY HOUSE

3

THE GUIDE TO COMMUNAL **LIVING**

DIGGERS & DREAMERS

94/95

Most Community members are active as paid and voluntary workers in projects aimed at meeting specific needs in the neighbourhood. These include employment development and organic gardening on reclaimed derelict land. Financially, we are self supporting. We live simply, sharing domestic tasks. Leadership is on a rotating basis and decisions are made jointly. We are looking for new people to join us as members or volunteers. There are no specific skill or age requirements. Length of membership commitment varies. For more information write to us at the above address or phone to arrange a visit. The wider Ashram Community of which this project is a part has about 80 members and meets twice yearly. It can be contacted at: Ashram Community Office, 239 Abbeyfield Road, Sheffield S4 7AW.

Status
existing community

Address
23-25 Grantham Road
Sparkbrook
BIRMINGHAM
B11 1LU

Telephone
021 773 7061

Number of over 18s
5

Number of under 18s
0

Year started
1976

Situation
urban

Ideological focus
Christian

Open to new members
Yes

BALNAKEIL CRAFT VILLAGE

THE GUIDE TO COMMUNAL **LIVING**

DIGGERS-&-DREAMERS

4

94/95

Status
existing community

Address
Durness
by LAIRG
Sutherland
IV27 4PT

Telephone
0971 511296

Number of over 18s
26

Number of under 18s
17

Year started
1964

Situation
rural remote

Ideological focus
pagan/new age/none/ecological

Open to new members
Yes

Balnakeil Craft Village is a well established craft and art centre located amid wild and spectacular mountain and coastal scenery. An ex-military base, the single storey, "billet-type" buildings are privately owned and occupied by a collection of children and adults. Our livelihood is largely provided for by the production and sale, to tourists, of craft and art work. Imaginatively converted, most buildings provide excellent facilities for workshops, shops, studios and living space. Within the larger community there are various levels of co-operation, from the essential to the speculative. Although we do not share income or living space, there is a high degree of sharing regarding skills and materials with informally shared childcare. There are also areas of common land, some of which is put to food production - our eating habits varying from vegetarian to omnivorous.

The craft village as a whole is without any formal structure and there is a tendency towards anarchic ways: decisions on matters that concern the craft community are usually arrived at by consensus. Education is provided for by a local primary school; although there is no local secondary school, one is due to open in 1995. At least one family unit is considering *Education Otherwise*, too.

There are currently (first half of 1993) two buildings for sale (one a café/restaurant, with living space, and the other a shop, workshop and living area) and Jack'n'Jills of all trades and/or proficient craftspeople may well be welcome, although this is by no means exclusive. Accommodation for visitors is minimal (particularly in the tourist season), a room or two here and there with shared facilities (negotiable rent) plus a hotel (charge not negotiable). Written enquiries should be made to Ian Reeve at 8 Balnakeil Craft Village and phone enquiries to Charlie or Gene at the number shown alongside.

Beech Hill is a spacious country house set in the rural heart of Devon. There are also a number of outbuildings converted for living in and for projects of interest to the co-op. We have seven acres of grounds and gardens. All cultivation is organically based and is largely focussed upon production of a wide variety of vegetables and fruits. We have a young vineyard, a plant nursery, an ancient walled garden and a large paddock. Providing accommodation and facilities for groups on courses and paying guests is a major source of income and we are expanding our activities in this area. Some of us earn a living outside and some work within the co-operative.

However, we are all involved, to a greater or lesser extent, in the co-op's overall plans and projects. To live here happily and effectively, people need goodwill, personal initiative, tolerance and stability. Dogmatism and preaching are definitely not wanted. Our intention is to go beyond narrow definitions of party politics, religious tradition and social structure. By thinking and acting co-operatively, we create unusual opportunities - for ourselves and for others - which improve the real quality of being and also enhance the circumstances in which we live. The co-operative's aims are summed up as follows:

1 To achieve maximum flexibility for individuals within collective policies
2 To try to find an optimum balance between private and collective ownership
3 To enable people to use and develop skills
4 To provide a meeting place where people can share ideas, information and experience
5 To create structures and opportunities which maximise possibilities within the current social and economic climate
6 To be aware of the impact of our work and lives on the environment and to develop projects accordingly.

At Beech Hill we aim to be a happy blend of rural peace and liveliness, honest work and restful leisure, philosophy and fun. We welcome visitors and ask that they write a short note about themselves (interests, background, etc) before coming. We will then send out further details about Beech Hill, together with suggested visiting dates.

BEECH HILL COMMUNITY

5

THE GUIDE TO COMMUNAL **LIVING**

DIGGERS & DREAMERS

94/95

Status
existing community

Address
Beech Hill House
Morchard Bishop
CREDITON
Devon
EX17 6RF

Telephone
0363 877587/877228

Number of over 18s
20

Number of under 18s
6

Year started
1983

Situation
rural

Ideological focus
ecological

Open to new members
Yes

BEESTON COMMUNITY HOUSE

THE GUIDE TO COMMUNAL **LIVING**

DIGGERS &- DREAMERS

6

94/95

Status
existing community

Address
4 Grange Avenue
Beeston
NOTTINGHAM
NG9 1GJ

Telephone
0602 223886 📞!

Number of over 18s
6

Number of under 18s

Year started
1975

Situation
suburban

Ideological focus
Christian

Open to new members
Yes

We live together in a big, slightly scruffy, Edwardian red-brick semi, sharing evening meals, bills, housework, a weekly communion and, at the moment, morning prayers. The Christian focus of the community is very much ecumenical, which involves us in ecumenical movements in the local churches as well as in accepting and trying to work with the differing ideas and expectations which our members have, about what being a Christian means and what community is for. People usually stay for two or three years, so this process of working out the rôle of the community and learning to accept one another is ongoing and leads to new conclusions from each new set of people.

Members of the house have ordinary outside occupations but are encouraged to get involved in the wider community in their spare time, in ways that put into practice their Christian beliefs. At the moment these practical involvements range from Sunday School teaching and preaching to work with the homeless, *Oxfam* and *Amnesty International*. In addition to this, one member of the community is "employed" by the other five to work full-time as a volunteer community worker. "Workers" (who stay for one or two years) have been involved recently with the homeless and badly housed, children, people with disabilities and campaigning, as well as at Nottingham University with the chaplaincy and *Student Community Action*.

Bhaktivedanta Manor is the main centre of the *International Society for Krishna Consciousness* in the UK. It is 17 acres of gardens, lake, woodland and pastures. Over 100 single students of Krishna consciousness study and serve at the Manor with other families participating also in daily services and activities. The spiritual focus is the worship of Radha-Krishna in the traditional Vaishnava style. All meals are lacto-vegetarian and the grounds supply a lot of the flowers and vegetables needed for the community. A herd of lifetime-protected cows and bulls provide the milk and the muscle for hauling and ploughing on the site.

The Manor is open for new members, but all devotees living on the property must be willing to comply with the basic standards of the community - no meat-eating, no intoxication of any type (including cigarettes, tea, coffee), no gambling and no pre- or extra-marital sex. The lifestyle of Krishna consciousness involves an awakening of the realisation that we are not these material bodies, we are the spirit soul within, the eternal children of God whom we know as Krishna. By chanting the holy names of Krishna and seving to our best capacity and devotion, we can uncover our true spiritual personalities and discover the pure love of God.

BHAKTI-VEDANTA MANOR

7

THE GUIDE TO COMMUNAL LIVING
DIGGERS -&- DREAMERS
94/95

Status
existing community

Address
Letchmore Heath
WATFORD
Hertfordshire
WD2 8EP

Telephone
0923 857244

Number of over 18s
150

Number of under 18s
40

Year started
1973

Situation
rural

Ideological focus
Vaishnava

Open to new members
Yes

BIRCHWOOD HALL COMMUNITY

THE GUIDE TO COMMUNAL **LIVING**

DIGGERS -&- DREAMERS

94/95

8

Status
existing community

Address
Storridge
MALVERN
Worcestershire
WR13 5EZ

Telephone

Number of over 18s
12

Number of under 18s
2

Year started
1970

Situation
rural

Ideological focus

Open to new members
Yes

Birchwood Hall is a housing co-operative occupying two separate buildings known as "The Coach House" and "The Main House". These operate as two separate entities, and the remainder of this description is concerned with the latter. The Main House group currently consists of ten adults, one child, and one infant, although additional people may soon join. Everyone here has paid employment, with some people working from home whilst others travel to Malvern, Worcester or Birmingham. Jobs are: Architect, designer, potter/audio-visual film-makers, civil servant, countryside ranger, milker, caterer, teacher, probation service worker, and University lecturer. Two college students also have Birchwood as their home, although they live away in term-time. We operate a degree of income sharing and children live here free. New members do not buy into the community, similarly they do not take out any money when they leave.

The Main House is a large Victorian edifice which now contains communal spaces including living and dining area, kitchen, television room, games room, laundry, workshop, and office. Individuals have their own room or share with a partner - there is quite a lot of personal space. Everyone takes a turn in cooking and aims to provide for individual's likes and dislikes (within reason!). The evening meal is the time when we all meet daily, and provides a regular point of contact for all members. Other shared pleasures include maintenance of the building and the sewage system, shopping, gardening, and cleaning, all tackled with varying degrees of enthusiasm. We have nine acres of land, mostly woodland. It is very beautiful and a struggle to keep in order. The communal vegetable garden is more productive than it has been for a long time, but we do not intend to be self-sufficient.

The group operates on regular weekly meetings - alternately "business" and "feelings" - and less regular individual sessions. Decisions are reached by consensus and we all value harmony within the group. There are a variety of reasons why people came to live at Birchwood, but simply we live with each other because we like each other most of the time. Separately, the community operates a small residential conference centre known as *Anybody's Barn*, details of which can be obtained from the same address.

Blackcurrent Housing Co-op owns two houses in Northampton town centre, ten minutes walk apart. The larger of the two has eight bedrooms and two large halls attached to it which used to be a dance school. Currently there are three adults and two children in the big house living communally and we are renting out the smaller house to students. We are committed to being open with each other emotionally and we support each other in growing as individuals. We share childcare informally and try to be as non-violent with our children and each other as we can in an attempt to raise more whole human beings with less of the emotional baggage most adults carry around. We educate ourselves and our children through living and learning all the time. We have a vegan kitchen but members of the community are not necessarily strictly vegan.

We regularly host meetings of local groups (*Animal Concern* etc) and organise events of our own including co-counselling courses, despair and empowerment weekends and non-violence camps. We have plans to make the halls even more accessible to the local community by doing some structural work and decorating. We are inviting local groups to join us in creating a management group to take responsibility for them. We envisage them being used for courses, groups, workshops, theatre groups, acoustic music etc. We only charge cost price for events we have here and try to keep those costs are low as possible to make them accessible to everyone.

We are looking for more members at the moment. Our ideal number is roughly six adults and two children. We want to live with people who have similar ideas but it is not essential that they are involved in everything we do as long as we can get on with each other and work out any problems. We also run an ethical investment scheme so if you want to invest in us do write and let us know! To give some idea of who we are; things we like include; gardening, jumble sales, dancing, table tennis, massage, woodstoves, singing, leek lasagne and co-counselling.

BLACK-CURRENT HOUSING CO-OP

9

THE GUIDE TO COMMUNAL **LIVING**
DIGGERS *&* DREAMERS
94/95

Status
existing community

Address
24 St Michael's Avenue NORTHAMPTON NN1 4JQ

Telephone
0604 33203

Number of over 18s
5

Number of under 18s
2

Year started
1988

Situation
urban

Ideological focus
co-operation (and fun)

Open to new members
Yes

BOTTON CAMPHILL COMMUNITY

THE GUIDE TO COMMUNAL LIVING

DIGGERS & DREAMERS

10

94/95

Status
in existence

Address
Botton Village
Danby
Whitby
North Yorkshire
YO21 2NJ

Telephone
0287 660871

Number of over 18s
260

Number of under 18s
50

Year started
1955

Situation
rural

Ideological focus
Anthroposophy

Open to new members
Yes

Botton Village started as part of *The Camphill Village Trust*. About half of the village population are mentally handicapped adults. The twenty-eight households, which vary in size from six to 18 persons, are run as extended families, with no separate staff quarters. The 610 acre land includes extensive forest and six bio-dynamic farms. No chemicals or artificials have been put on the land since Botton started.

There is no conventional management strata to the organisation of the village. It is run by lots of groups. There are no salaries or wages. Workshops and services include bakery, cheese making, glass engraving, wood workshop, doll-making, weaving, candle making, Post Office and shops. There is also a Waldorf School for children from the area and a retirement home for the elderly.

Although we are basically Christian and try to follow the principles of philosophy as propounded by Rudolf Steiner we totally accept the freedom of each individual to discover his or her own path of destiny. In a community of human beings working together the well being of the community will be the greater the less the individual claims for himself the proceeds of the work he has done himself. In fact, our requirements are satisfied by the work done by others when we make over the proceeds of our own work to our fellow workers.

Magic and Brambles are, respectively, an inner city resource centre and a housing co-operative, based in two houses in Sheffield. We are committed to promoting co-operation and co-operatives in the local community; anti-sexist work and libertarian education supporting children and adults in learning outside of schools. There is a resources office, a meeting space for community groups and a large wildlife garden. One building acts as a men's house promoting anti-sexist work, providing a supportive space for men to work through their isolation and sexism.

We are a mixed co-op, eat communally and income share. All work is shared including childcare. Members of the co-op are expected to work for 20 hours a week for the project and we are keen to involve people from the local community. A mediation scheme is run from the resource centre. We are looking for new members - no money or curriculum vitae required, just energy and commitment to genuine co-operation. We are part of *Radical Routes* Secondary Co-op and are interested in links with other groups and co-ops working for mutual aid and sustainable change. Visitors are welcome but only by prior arrangement.

BRAMBLES HOUSING CO-OP/ MAGIC

11

THE GUIDE TO COMMUNAL **LIVING**
DIGGERS *&* DREAMERS
94/95

Status
existing community

Address
82 Andover Street
Burngreave
SHEFFIELD
S3 9EH

Telephone
0742 797164 ☏!

Number of over 18s
4

Number of under 18s
2

Year started
1992

Situation
urban

Ideological focus
co-operation

Open to new members
Yes

BRAZIERS ADULT COLLEGE

Status
existing community

Address
Braziers Park
IPSDEN
Oxfordshire
OX10 6AN

Telephone
0491 680221

Number of over 18s
15

Number of under 18s
0

Year started
1950

Situation
rural

Ideological focus
evolutionist

Open to new members
Yes

Braziers is a resident community and a non-resident network of interested associates and members. It was founded in 1950 as a registered Friendly Society with the official title of "Braziers Park School of Integrative Social Research". The main aim is to carry out group research into positive health and holistic living, seeking new ways of working and thinking together which could offer hope of further human progress. As part of this research and, at the same time, to have a constructive social activity which helps provide an added source of income for the group, its facilities and amenities are made open to the public as a residential adult education college for weekend seminars and summer schools. Such courses, besides exploring subjects which can further the aim of social research, provide opportunities for people to learn and develop new insights and leisure skills. In this capacity Braziers is a member of the *Adult Residential Colleges Association*. The community regularly includes a number of British and overseas student volunteers who, during four decades, have helped establish Braziers as an international education centre with a reputation which reaches to many parts of the world. We should add that, besides a large house and some cottages the community is responsible for some 50 acres (26ha) including an organic garden and home farm. The produce helps make the community partly self-sufficient.

Despite initial difficulties such as threaten any new social venture - including having to encounter and transcend schismatic trends - the community has been able, slowly, to work out new methods of democratic communication and structure, guided when ever possible by knowledge available from sociology, social psychology and the understanding of psycho-social evolution. From our experience has emerged a method of self-counselling and self governance which Braziers calls "the sensory-executive synthesis". Booklets and research papers which record and explain the method are available on sale from Braziers. The Braziers group is ready to consider new recruits and interested visitors for short or long periods, subject to previous written application. Information leaflets and application forms are vailable from the Warden's Office.

The Cambridge Buddhist Centre is the public centre for *Friends of the Western Buddhist Order* to attend. The Centre has moved to new and bigger premises on Newmarket Road, a few doors up from the previous address. There are also five community houses - four men's and one women's - with altogether about 35 people living in them, all of whom are practising Buddhists. The first community in Cambridge was started in 1987 and more people have joined every year since. There are two businesses associated with the Centre, a wholesale business supplying jewellery and gifts to retailers, and a shop selling the goods. Many of the community residents work in the businesses. People who live in the Centre and work in the business receive a small income for personal items, and those who do not work in the business pay for board and lodging themselves.

The communities are gradually expanding and the people who join come through their involvement with Buddhism. In communities members find it easier to put into practice the Buddhist principles of non-violence, truthful and gentle speech, friendship, mindfulness, simplicity and contentment. Being part of the spiritual community allows openness and trust to develop. Each house may organise itself slightly differently, but share certain features: a morning meditation together when possible and at least one evening a week shared together. At the moment there are no communities with children. Weekend retreats in country locations are organised regularly for the people coming to the meditation or Buddhism classes at the Centre which are open to the public. These retreats allow a sampling of community living for a short period.

CAMBRIDGE BUDDHIST CENTRE

13

THE GUIDE TO COMMUNAL LIVING

DIGGERS *&* DREAMERS

94/95

Status
in existence

Address
19 Newmarket Road
CAMBRIDGE
CB5 8EG

Telephone
0223 460252

Number of over 18s
35

Number of under 18s
0

Year started
1987

Situation
urban

Ideological focus
Buddhist

Open to new members
Yes

CANON FROME COMMUNITY

THE GUIDE TO
COMMUNAL
LIVING
DIGGERS
&
DREAMERS

14

94/95

Status
existing community

Address
LEDBURY
Herefordshire
HR8 2TD

Telephone

Number of over 18s
29

Number of under 18s
25

Year started
1978

Situation
rural

Ideological focus
ecological

Open to new members
Yes

Canon Frome Court is a converted Georgian mansion and stable block set in 35 acres of farm land and formal gardens. We occupy self-contained living spaces within the main house or stable block. The estate is owned by the *Windflower Housing Association* and each living unit is purchased leasehold at prices commensurate with the local housing market. We share large communal areas which include meeting rooms, guest bedrooms, gardens, swimming pool, lake and even a shop. Part of the main house is dedicated for use of events, this area consists of a large kitchen, toilet facilities, living/meeting room and gymnasium. Members are financially independent working within or outside the community, and some receive state benefits.

We do not have a fixed ideological focus, the diversity adding to the richness of our existence. Communal life centres around the running of our organic mixed farm and garden, maintaining the estate, enjoying our beautiful environment, craft activities, hosting outside events and workshops. A weekly Circle Dancing evening (anyone welcome) and visits to the theatre, cinema and local hostelry proving popular with some. We meet twice a week, once for a communal meal and once for a meeting. The meetings deal with business matters or community and personal issues. We try, whenever possible, to make our decisions by consensus. Our children are formally educated in state or Waldorf scholls. We welcome visitors and have regular *WWOOF* weekends, offering an ideal introduction to our way of life.

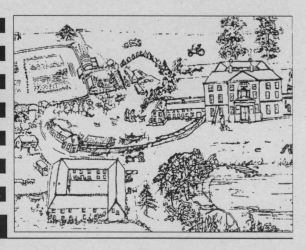

In addition to the exhibition and displays the Llwyngwern Quarry is also home to a small residential community, made up of people who work at the Centre for Alternative Technology.

Structure: intentionally informal
Economic relations: life sustaining activities are funded jointly and equally except by people who are age challenged
Approaches to decision making: tangential and Kropotkinite except when something needs to be done
Childcare and education: we all play with the children until their parents come and take them away
Diet and eating habits: very low meat diet
Types of work: varied
Types of building and land: rural industrial reclaimed site with modified 19th Century industrial cottages plus some new build
Private space: we all have some
Legal structure: none
Special feature: tenancy is tied to working for the Centre for Alternative Technology
Postal enquiries: via the Centre for Alternative Technology only

CENTRE FOR ALTERNATIVE TECHNOLOGY

15

THE GUIDE TO
COMMUNAL
LIVING
DIGGERS & DREAMERS

94/95

Status
existing community

Address
Llwyngwern Quarry
MACHYNLLETH
Powys
SY20 9AZ

Telephone
0654 702924

Number of over 18s
12

Number of under 18s
3

Year started
1975

Situation
rural

Ideological focus
pragmatism

Open to new members

CENTRE FOR HOLISTIC LIVING

THE GUIDE TO
COMMUNAL
LIVING
DIGGERS
-&-
DREAMERS
94/95

16

Status
embryonic community

Address
care of
169 Gloucester Road
CROYDON
Surrey
CR0 2DW

Telephone

Number of over 18s
10

Number of under 18s

Year started

Situation
semi-rural

Ideological focus
deep ecology

Open to new members
Yes

We have a very strong, holistic, Green commitment, both practically and spiritually. We are committed to resolving conflict in a constructive way. We believe that, whatever happens in life, we have drawn towards us, to make use of as we choose. We want to have fun and celebrate life. We see creativity as a vital part of our vision - practising various arts and crafts and creating a beautiful environment to live and work in

On childcare and education, we want to work with nature, in terms of a child's natural abilities and development. We want to help children to feel empowered, in control of their own lives, intuitively finding their path in life. We believe a large part of childcare can be "non-activity", with the children learning as we work and play - children only learn happily what they want to learn. We can trust children to know what is best for themselves and that they won't hurt themselves or others. We can provide them with their needs, allow them to take the independence they need at any stage, but also give them the boundaries they need. With this in mind, we want to set up a natural childbirth/childcare information, support and education centre - drop-in groups, day courses, residential courses etc. We want to run courses/workshops on green issues, arts and crafts, natural health, personal growth etc.

We also want artists and craftspeople to live and/or work with us, displaying their work in an on-site shop. Maybe also: Green shop; organic café; natural health centre; arts centre. In short, our vision is to help our children survive in the World and the World survive for our children. Capital is desirable initially, but not essential. When you write to us, please tell us about yourselves and your ideas.

Common Ground is a group of radical co-operatives based in inner Birmingham. We have a housing co-op - New Education - which houses people involved in various co-operative and radical activities. Anyone joining needs to be prepared to work an average minimum of 20 hours a week on such activities in order to be housed. We have workers' co-ops operating in the following areas: vegan/veggie catering; wholefood café, T-shirt printing, organic vegetable growing and delivery. Co-ops are also setting up in the areas of building and wholefood cash and carry and delivery.

We own a large high street shop front and are possibly looking to buy a warehouse to house the co-ops and act as a radical centre for Birmingham. Some tenants are also involved in counselling and political work. The co-ops aim to provide basic wages and raise money to fund other co-operative developments and political campaigns/groups. We are part of *Radical Routes* - a national secondary co-operative (a co-op of co-ops) and very involved in its ethical investment scheme.

COMMON GROUND

THE GUIDE TO COMMUNAL LIVING

DIGGERS & DREAMERS

94/95

Status
existing community

Address
24 South Road
Hockley
BIRMINGHAM
B18 5NB

Telephone
021 551 1679

Number of over 18s
22

Number of under 18s
3

Year started
1986

Situation
urban

Ideological focus
anarchist

Open to new members
Yes

COMMUNITIES
IN EAST
LANCASHIRE/
BURNLEY-
WOOD
HOUSING
CO-OP

THE GUIDE TO
COMMUNAL
LIVING
DIGGERS
-&-
DREAMERS

18

94/95

Status
existing community

Address
care of
39 Kirkgate
BURNLEY
Lancashire
BB11 3NL

Telephone
0282 36932

Number of over 18s
7

Number of under 18s
7

Year started
1986

Situation
urban

Ideological focus

Open to new members
Yes

COMMUNITIES IN EAST LANCASHIRE

In East Lancashire there is a network of actually existing communities and a group(s) that is in the process of forming. We see ourselves as a loose knit community of people who share activities, interests and objectives in common. In 1973 People in Common (PiC) bought some houses in Burnley as an intital low cost base, and later in 1977 aquired a derelict cornmill on the outskirts of town. A building co-operative was formed to renovate both the houses in Burnley and the cornmill at Altham,

Burnleywood Housing Co-operative came about as a sort of bi-product of People in Common, in the same way that the space programme led to the non-stick frying pan! In terms of buildings we have six terraced houses, quite near to each other. In two cases two houses are in fact joined to each other. Since it was launched the co-op has developed gradually as an unintentional community, with new people joining over the years some of whom had previously been involved with PiC. We have meetings and socials once a month. We also have regular "working days" on the repairs of the houses. The women in the co-op who have much knowledge and experience of manual skills have taken a leading rôle on these occasions. The emphasis is on individualism with people living their own lives as they see best, in separate households, or even as indivilualists within a household. People co-operate as and when seems appropriate. Individuals have links with Altham and are also involved in projects within the wider community such as the local credit union, the wholefood co-operative, Woodcraft Folk, and "Trees for Burnley". People in the co-op have a wide variety of interests such as political and enviromental issues, looking after children, playing and watching football, putting on puppet shows, juggling, brewing home-made beer and wine, walking, cycling and recycling, and digging and dreaming on our allotment (or in the case of the permaculturists - dreaming and not digging!). We do have space available from time to time and can usually accommodate visitors. If you are interested in an an alternative lifestyle that is not too demanding or too structured, then this might just possibly be the place for you.

as well as doing outside income generating work. Some of the people involved moved to the now renovated mill, while others stayed in Burnley in the guise of Burnleywood Housing Co-op. In 1989 Altham Hardwood Centre was set up involving people from both groups. It is an ecologically sound workers' co-op, kilning, machining and selling native hardwoods. In recent years PiC has expanded into a wider network including the Mill group, the housing co-op in Burnley and embryonic other group(s).

We are the members of PiC Housing Co-op committed to the development of the cornmill as the home of an income sharing commune. Further building work is necessary to complete new accommodation. We expect to have at least twelve bedrooms when all is done. *Altham Hardwood Centre* has workshop and storage space within the mill and we share office, kitchen/dining facilities with them. There are about four acres of land, including riverbank, in which we are developing kitchen, ornamental and wildlife aspects as well as varied play spaces. All gardening is organic. At weekends and in holidays the adults are usually out-numbered by the children. We neither have nor want any pets.

We have a strong committment to co-operation, equality and left, global and ecological perspectives. Our enthusiasms include Bridge, cycling, woodcarving, stargazing, radical politics, childplay, computer and rôle-playing games and of course building and gardening. We still read *The Guardian*. Our cooking habits range from vegetarian through omnivore to Marmitarian. We are looking for practically minded people who wish to live communally in a relatively structured way. A willingness to help with the building work is essential (skilled or unskilled). We are keen to expand yet are looking for people able to give a long term commitment to the project, so we are fairly cautious when it comes to accepting new provisional members. If this interests you and you would like to visit please write with some information about yourself.

18

THE GUIDE TO COMMUNAL **LIVING**
DIGGERS & DREAMERS
94/95

Status
existing community

Address
Altham Corn Mill
Burnley Road
Altham
ACCRINGTON
Lancashire
BB5 5UP

Telephone

Number of over 18s
5

Number of under 18s
3

Year started
1973

Situation
semi rural

Ideological focus
eclectic

Open to new members
Yes

COMMUNITIES IN EAST LANCASHIRE/ NEW COMMUNITY

THE GUIDE TO COMMUNAL **LIVING**

DIGGERS *&* DREAMERS

18

94/95

Status
embryonic community

Address
care of
Altham Cornmill
Burnley Rd, Altham
ACCRINGTON
Lancashire
BB5 5UP

Telephone
0282 770707

Number of over 18s

Number of under 18s

Year started

Situation
semi-rural

Ideological focus

Open to new members
Yes

We are developing a new community with the aim of extending the benefits and advantages of a co-operative lifestyle to a larger more diverse number of people than is possible in a small close communal group. We envisage that the community will be anywhere up to 75 people and would be an open ended network of co-operative and communal groups, families and individuals sharing whatever aspects of their lives are important at any one time. The emphasis will be on choice, opting in and out as individuals needs and wants change.

Co-operation: We plan that people will live in a variety of home situations - from single family units to small living groups (either rented or owner occupied) and that with the numbers of people involved such schemes as food co-ops; car pools; shared childcare; LETS schemes; work situations ... will develop.

Social Aspects: In a community of this size there will be the added social advantages of shared interests and friendship and the chance to create a local social life - our own community centre; Music/ Dance/Theatre groups; women's groups; meditation; therapy ...

Self-build Project: We are currently investigating various local self-build sites as ways of providing housing/workshops/community buildings. These would be built using simple enviroment friendly techniques that allow unskilled people to build their own homes.

If this kind of community appeals to you and you would like further details of the various ideas mentioned above then please write to Chris Coates, Catriona Stamp and Malcolm Cockcroft at the address alongside.

L'Arche Communities are scattered around the world, and also around the UK: in Canterbury, Inverness, Liverpool, Lambeth, Bognor Regis, Brecon and Edinburgh; and there are communities in Cork and Kilkenny in the Republic of Ireland. How to satisfy "the powers that be", as registered houses for "people with learning disabilities", without losing our freedom and simplicity - living together one-to-one in small families as brothers and sisters? Where people are welcomed and affirmed, undreamed of capacities unfold, as people really grow. These things happen at work, as well as home. We don't just need house assistants; we are looking for people interested in using their skills in craft workshops, and in horticultural schemes.

Living in a l'Arche Community means a challenge to live in close relationships, learning the true meaning of forgiveness. Community means a house is "home" for everyone there, whatever length of time they stay. Community means eating together, celebrating together and praying together, sharing the tasks of daily living - cooking, doing the dishes, going shopping. But there is time off, private space, as well. There are good in-service training opportunities, which could even lead to qualifications and a decent job! Things are decided democratically through Community Councils. These communities are Christian in practice (and connected to the wider church) but nothing is imposed and those of other faiths or none are really welcomed. No qualifications are asked for; but this life is not for everyone, and a "trial visit" of a few days is necessary.

COMMUNITIES OF L'ARCHE

19

THE GUIDE TO COMMUNAL **LIVING**
DIGGERS & DREAMERS
94/95

Status
network

Address
10 Briggate
Silsden
KEIGHLEY
Yorkshire
BD20 9JT

Telephone
0535 656186

Number of over 18s
150

Number of under 18s
4

Year started
1976

Situation
urban

Ideological focus
Christian (Buddhist in African Communities)

Open to new members
Yes

COMMUNITY CREATION

THE GUIDE TO
COMMUNAL
LIVING
DIGGERS
-&-
DREAMERS

20

94/95

Status
embryonic community

Address
care of
45 Alsom Avenue
WORCESTER PARK
Surrey
KT4 7EG

Telephone
081 330 5461

Number of over 18s

Number of under 18s

Year started
1990

Situation
urban

Ideological focus
Green

Open to new members

The Community Creation Trust, founded and directed by Julie Lowe, is now established as a charity dedicated to environmental education, in building design and human behaviour generally. The Trust has been given a four-year lease of a 1.5 acre site behind Kings Cross Station, London, with buildings which include a long concrete barn.

Here the Battle Bridge Centre is coming to life. Timber chalets will be constructed to house 16 homeless people and to create within the barn a green village with a vegetarian restaurant, conservatory, resource centre, shops, offices, workshops and the RAJA Project, a holistic health service offering a wide range of therapies and including a detoxification programme. A large auditorium in the centre of the barn will be used for exhibitions, fairs and inter-faith events. A demonstration eco-house will be open to school children and other visitors. The development has started on site with the aid of volunteers and gifts of materials and cash.

The aim is to address specific local problems, which include homelessness, drug addiction, unemployment, and partially derelict locality; and to offer some services to a wider public via the eco-house and Raja. The Trust is also helping to set up a resource centre in Tamil Nadu, India. Offers of help or participation in any shape or form are welcome.

The Community of St Clare is a small Anglican contemplative, enclosed community for women, founded in 1950. Life vows are normally taken after some years of testing the life. Work includes work in the garden, growing fruit and vegetables, work in the printing house and wafer bakery (for communion wafers) and the necessary house work, cooking and laundry for the community in the convent and for visitors to our guest-house which is well used by individuals and groups who come for retreats or simply for quiet and refreshment.

The Community is in the Franciscan tradition and decisions are made by the community as a whole. It is one of a group of communities and is kept in touch with many situations throughout the world by the Brothers of St Francis, the Sisters of the Community of St Francis and the members of the Third Order, as well as by the people who come to the guest-house and the requests for prayer which are received by letter or phone. Those wishing to join us should be over 21, in good health, and drawn to a community life with prayer as a central concern. Enquiries about the guest-house should be made by post or by phone (between 6.00 and 7.00pm).

COMMUNITY OF ST CLARE

21

THE GUIDE TO COMMUNAL LIVING

DIGGERS & DREAMERS

94/95

Status
existing community

Address
St Mary's Convent
Freeland
WITNEY
Oxfordshire
OX7 8AJ

Telephone
0993 881225

Number of over 18s
14

Number of under 18s
0

Year started
1950

Situation
rural

Ideological focus
Christian

Open to new members
Yes

CRABAPPLE COMMUNITY

THE GUIDE TO
COMMUNAL
LIVING
DIGGERS &
DREAMERS
94/95

22

Status
existing community

Address
Berrington Hall
Berrington
SHREWSBURY
Shropshire
SY5 6HA

Telephone

Number of over 18s
7

Number of under 18s
4

Year started
1975

Situation
rural

Ideological focus
ecological, feminist
etc

Open to new members
Yes

We are an income sharing, rural community living in a large Georgian house with 20 acres of land. Most of our income comes from our wholefood shop in Shrewsbury (4 miles away) where we each work about 2 days a week. After the shop and domestic work, which are both shared fairly equally there is farming, gardening, building work, vehicle repairs, paperwork etc. to be done where we specialise more. Our land is farmed organically, we have 2 Jersey cows, Jacob sheep, chickens, ducks and bees. We make cheese, butter and yoghurt for our own consumption. We have a large walled garden where we grow most of our own fruit and vegetables. Our farming policy has been to not keep any animals solely for meat, but any bull calves, ram lambs etc are available as a meat alternative to our largely vegetarian diet. We have had vegans living here but we recognise that vegans and dairy farming don't mix easily! We occasionally have groups camping here and we are interested in developing this but we have very little room for courses etc. The house is in a reasonable state of repair but there is always work to be done on it. We have communal vehicles plus many bikes. In the last few years we have planted trees, fitted solar panels, re-designed the garden and fitted out a new laundry and dairy. We are presently setting up a pottery. In the next few years we are hoping to have more people, do up extra accommodation, set up more income sources, grow more veg for sale, plant lots more trees! We like to feel that we are open to change, our communal experience ranges from a few months to 12 years but we are all still experimenting and we have got a lot to learn. Although we work fairly hard we also like to relax. We brew our own beer and wine, have occasional sweat lodges, massage evenings, group outings etc and there is always music around. Most of the house is a non smoking zone. We are less isolated than many rural communities and are involved in and/or are supportive of local womens, peace, environmental, anti-fascist and gay groups. Our children are looked after primarily by their parents with plenty of back-up. They all attend local schools. Our approaches to life vary and we have no easily definable common aim but many of our interests are shared. We are not looking for any particular people or skills, whether we can get on with you or not is more important. We try to work by consensus and share out responsibilities and decision making as much as possible. No money is needed to join, all bills etc. are paid communally and all members receive pocket money and a holiday allowance. If interested please write (with an sae).

The Bruderhof Community began in Germany in 1920 just after the First World War but our roots go back 460 years to the radical reformation, indeed we feel especially akin to the Early Christians of the first 200 years AD and we seek to live like them. There are Bruderhof Communities in England, Germany, the United States of America and Canada. Membership in the Bruderhof requires a lifetime commitment.

Our first call is to Christ and this cannot be separated from the brothers and sisters to whom we are pledged. We do not feel that any one pattern for daily life is the answer, but we do believe in a life of Christian brotherhood that comes from an inner change of heart. The one desire of all is to follow Jesus completely in every aspect of life. The Bruderhof children are educated up to high-school age by members in our own schools.

The manufacture of nursery play equipment and equipment for the handicapped is the principal means of livelihood. Inquiries are welcomed. Visits can be arranged but please write in advance so as to ensure accommodation. Guests are asked to share in the work and life in an open and seeking way. Our urgent longing and hope is that all men and women on this Earth will one day live in true justice and brotherhood under the rulership of God.

DARVELL BRUDERHOF COMMUNITY

23

THE GUIDE TO COMMUNAL **LIVING**
DIGGERS &
DREAMERS

94/95

Status
existing community

Address
Hutterian Brethren
ROBERTSBRIDGE
East Sussex
TN32 5DR

Telephone
0580 880626

Number of over 18s
140

Number of under 18s
140

Year started
1920

Situation
rural

Ideological focus
Christian

Open to new members
Yes

EARTHWORM

Earthworm Housing Co-op has lived and worked at Wheatstone since January 1989. There are seven acres of fertile land set in a beautiful valley with a large house and out-buildings. We aim to explore and promote ecological lifestyles. We try to minimise our use of products involving human, animal and environmental exploitation. We are communally vegan and share a vegan kitchen. We share our income. We welcome children and are supportive in shared childcare and home education. Household decisions are made by consensus at weekly meetings. We farm the land veganically - without the use of chemicals or animal products/labour. We have three vegetable and herb gardens providing food for ourselves and guests. We are planting trees and exploring permaculture and forest garden techniques. Eventually we hope to gain some income from our gardens, but there is still a lot of work to do re-claiming neglected land. We aim to use alternative energy and appropriate technology. We recycle as much waste as we can and now use composting toilets. Wood is used for cooking, heating and hot water; we eat organic food and use alternative medicines and therapies.

Before our arrival the building had been vandalised and neglected; we have done a lot of restoration but accommodation is still very basic. We are always working towards a more energy efficient and comfortable home and workplace. We have a large field and fully equipped campers/catering kitchen which is available to groups for camps, courses and workshops. We have already hosted several events ranging from a permaculture course to Green Gatherings. We hope to expand as a venue. If you are interested in facilities, please contact us. Earthworm is part of the *Radical Routes* network of housing and workers' co-ops. We operate a loan stock system to raise money for restoring the property and expanding our projects. If you wish to invest in us (we pay interest) please contact us for further details and a loan stock form. We are open to new members, subject to availability of space and a trial period living here. Please enclose a stamped addressed envelope when you write to us.

Status	
existing community	
Address	
Wheatstone	
Leintwardine	
CRAVEN ARMS	
Shropshire	
SH7 0LP	
Telephone	
Number of over 18s	
8	
Number of under 18s	
4	
Year started	
1989	
Situation	
rural	
Ideological focus	
ecological	
Open to new members	
Yes	

The Erraid community is a financially independent and self supporting part of the *Findhorn Foundation*. We are a spiritual community and the thread that brings us together is our desire for a holistic quality of life and a greater expression of our divinity. Meditation plays an important part in our lives, helping us to discover the right action for ourselves as individuals and for the community as a whole. Erraid is an island on the south-western tip of Mull in the Inner Hebrides. Its one square mile displays the physical features typical of this part of Scotland, where granite outcrops and peat bogs support an abundance of wild flowers. The climate can be extremely variable.

We live in a five acre walled settlement with cottages, outbuildings and enclosed gardens. The resident group on Erraid consists of around ten members. We have always had a mix of single people, couples and families - children thrive here. Each member has a distinct area of focus within the community. Because of our small number, we often work together, turning our hands to whatever needs to be done. Meals are generally communal and mostly vegetarian much of our food coming from our organic gardens, our dairy cows, poultry and the sea. Throughout most of the year we share our homes with guests aware that our community serves an educational purpose for all who come here. We welcome enquiries from people interested in participation in our life and work.

ISLE OF ERRAID COMMUNITY

25

THE GUIDE TO
COMMUNAL
LIVING
DIGGERS &
DREAMERS
94/95

Status
existing community

Address
Isle of Erraid
Fionnphort
Isle of Mull
Argyll
PA66 6BN

Telephone
06817 384

Number of over 18s
9

Number of under 18s
4

Year started
1978

Situation
rural

Ideological focus
spiritual

Open to new members
Yes

Drawing: Anne Whitbread

FAMILY TREE COMMUNITY

THE GUIDE TO COMMUNAL LIVING
DIGGERS -&- DREAMERS
94/95

26

Family Tree is a small Christian community set up to provide accommodation and care for adults with learning disabilities. We live in a large house overlooking Hackney Downs. Newton Housing Association own the house and have renovated it for us. So it is now suitable for people in wheel chairs, and includes a chapel at the heart of the house, where we meet for prayer and worship.

Currently (the first half of 1993) we have three adults with disabilities, four tenants, one full time worker and a volunteer. We are looking for another to join us. Each tenant pays a weekly rent to include all bills and food. Supper is a communal meal. Individual incomes are needed. Some people go out to work while others receive Income Support. We are equal opportunist and enjoy the benefits of simple shared living. If you would like to know more about us or come for a visit please write to Karen Simpson at the above address and we will look forward to welcoming you.

Status
existing community

Address
1 Queensdown Road
Hackney
LONDON
E5 8NN

Telephone
081 985 6908

Number of over 18s
8

Number of under 18s

Year started
1980

Situation
urban

Ideological focus
Christian

Open to new members
Yes

We have a very structured life in our communities and those who have visited our communities often comment on how we are the most organised communal group they have seen. We have been told that our communal structure is like that of a kibbutz, our children have their schooling together in their age groups on the property of the commune, with community teachers following a home schooling programme. As they become older they begin to learn certain trades within the commune (such as child care and teaching, cooking and home management, computer skills, secretarial and office skills, mechanics, house repairs and maintenance, carpentry, electrical work) and then also we have training in evangelising others to the Christian faith. The daily schedule usually consists of all adults coming together for a short devotional reading after breakfast and then breaking up to go to their respective duties. Once a week there is a council meeting where all those aged 16 and up attend to make united decisions on policies pertaining to the individual commune. Decisions rane across all subjects from changes in scheduling, aspects of the commune that someone feels need to be changed etc. The main body that oversees the running of one of our communities is called Teamwork and consists of at least three members who manifest leadership qualities in each area of the organisation of the community: ie one member is personally involved in the personnel of the community and in making sure that they are happy and satisfied in their duties and that they have their needs met as well as being good at general home care etc; one person is involved in the department of child care and is more or less an "expert" in that field; one member is a good business person in finances and general business sense. With this sort of team working together to oversee the community we have found that a good balance is kept in the running of the house. This Teamwork meets on a daily basis and can discuss anything from bringing up the meals to a better standard, the excursion for the weekend for the teenagers, bills that need to be paid, or obtaining better teaching materials for one of the classes. The basis of our community is Christian and it is why we live communally, as we believe living in this way is in obediance to the scriptures and also is much more effective in our missionary efforts to evangelise others (nb by evangelising others we do not mean forcing them to join our commune, but simply affirming faith in Jesus Christ in one's own life). Weekends are for personal families to spend time in their own family unit.

THE FAMILY

27

THE GUIDE TO COMMUNAL **LIVING**
DIGGERS & DREAMERS
94/95

Status
network

Address
BM Box 8440
LONDON
WC1N 3XX

Telephone
071 435 4934

Number of over 18s

Number of under 18s

Year started
1971

Situation

Ideological focus
Christian

Open to new members

FINDHORN FOUNDATION

Status
existing community

Address
Cluny Hill College
FORRES
Morayshire
IV36 0RD

Telephone
0309 673655

Electronic mail
treesforlife@gn.apc.org

Number of over 18s
130

Number of under 18s
22

Year started
1962

Situation
urban & rural

Ideological focus
spiritual

Open to new members
Yes

The Findhorn Foundation is an international spiritual community in north-east Scotland. It was founded in 1962 by Eileen and Peter Caddy and Dorothy Maclean on the principles that God, or the source of life, is accessible to each of us at all times, and that nature, including the planet, has intelligence and is part of a much larger plan. While we have no formal doctrine or creed, we believe an evolutionary expansion of consciousness is taking place in the world, creating a human culture infused with spiritual values.

The Foundation, a charitable trust, is a centre of education and demonstration. It began with three adults and three children in a barren corner of a caravan park and now includes approximately 150 resident members of varying ages and nationalities living in several sites in the area. A wider community or 'village' is growing here as people with shared values and vision are coming to live alongside the Foundation. We invite you to join us in the experience of our living education. Come and help us create a positive vision and future for humanity and the planet! Information about workshops, conferences and guest programmes are available from the Accommodation Secretary.

Gaunts House is a growing "new way" community within an old traditional rural one on the estate. Our vision, aim and intent is to evolve an environment for learning, excellence and sharing. Gaunts House is an extensive period mansion. The estate consists of rolling Dorset farmland, woods, river, a lake, quarries, about 55 dwellings, traditional farms and the centres: Gaunts House, Ashton Lodge, Hinton Retreat and High Lea, used for courses, conferences, seminars, and workshops, organised by external like-minded organisations and by the *Glyn Foundation*, our educational trust. Our courses deal with healing ourselves and the planet, spiritual development, personal growth, ecological awareness, care and concern for each other and for the environment, creativity, the arts and similar interests. The work here is organised through sub-groups, each largely carrying responsibility for their own planning and achievement. Groups meet regularly and are co-ordinated through House meetings. We take most of our important decisions by consensus, together.

We are in our fourth year and our numbers are slowly increasing. We often need more people to live and work with us permanently and seasonally - whatever your skills and interests, there may be a place for you. We have a process toward community membership, as we are selective about whom we invite to share our life and work here. People may come in a number of ways - please enquire. We have a free bed and board scheme for young adults on a half-day "energy exchange" basis. Our work is balanced with creativity in our living. Our general practice is to input seriously for half a day, and pursue our own interests for the other half, be that meeting in groups, playing, creating, studying, spending time alone and with families and so on. We share lunches together. Our main meals are vegetarian. Smoking is restricted to some areas. The rewards of living here are personal and pragamatic: high motivation and stimulation, time, space, encouragement and support to develop your own interests, and progress your "path". You won't grow rich financially; but you'll have the opportunity to talk openly and to develop those parts of you that only your centre can reach.

GAUNTS HOUSE COMMUNITY

29

THE GUIDE TO COMMUNAL LIVING

DIGGERS *&* DREAMERS

94/95

Status
existing community

Address
WIMBORNE
Dorset
BH21 4JQ

Telephone
0202 841522

Number of over 18s
25

Number of under 18s
6

Year started
1990

Situation
rural

Ideological focus
holistic

Open to new members
Yes

GIROSCOPE CO-OP

Status
existing community

Address
46 Wellstead Street
Hessle Road
HULL
HU3 3AQ

Telephone
0482 223376

Number of over 18s

Number of under 18s

Year started
1985

Situation
urban

Ideological focus
mixed

Open to new members
Yes

Giroscope workers' co-operative is an organisation providing housing for its workers and also low paid and unemployed young people. We also attempt to develop other co-ops as part of our plan for world domination. Workers of Giroscope are paid dole wages for a 30 hour week of mainly house renovation and maintenance (training given). Allowances are made for people with kids. We have 20 houses of various sizes housing people with a range of involvement in our work. We also have a crêche running three days a week for tenants and workers.

We have recently leased a shop to a co-op setting up a wholefood-cum-corner shop - *The People's Trading Company*. In the past we assisted a group set up a screen printing co-op. We are currently working with a group setting up a housing co-op. Out of all this a community is developing although most people live in their own homes or in shared houses. We have a fair amount of inter-action with the local community and have not set ourselves aside. We plan to continue developing our community, helping people to create their own housing and employment in a non-exploitative way. Ideologically we are mixed, inspired by Colin Ward's *Anarchy in Action* some people have got into green politics, some into Stalinism! We are mostly vegetarian and believe in low pay, equality, co-operatives and a good game of table tennis. Visitors welcome but write first to arrange accommodation - oh, and expect to work if staying more than an hour.

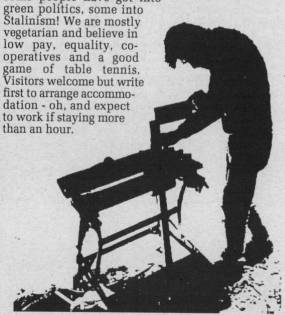

In our eighteenth year, our ideas seem to be settled somewhat. We mix published ideas with intuition to grow our own food, pay our own bills, teach our own children, raise our own animals and keep our forty-four acres in good heart. We manage our woodland to produce an eventual sustainable fuel. We have no other natural sources of power apart from our sweat and help from Neddy and Ben the donkeys, the bicycles, the van, the tractor, the JCB and the oil-fired central heating system-cum-clothes dryer-cum-cheese humidifier and mouse warmer. We service solid fuel cookers and make and sell lovely pottery from our shop to pay our mortgage; and we income share to level our luck to keep us equal.

We have no managers - we have pockets of autonomy - hats we wear. We have meetings and we eat together, there are several communal rooms and we cook and clean by rota. We each have our own room. WWOOFers sometime have to share. We eat vegetables and meat and find it difficult feeding vegans. We process our own waste, so if you plan to visit, we would appreciate it if you refrain from ingesting questionable chemicals and semi-toxins. We do not keep dogs but have lots of cats, rats, mice, squirrels, chickens, ducks, pigeons, slugs, cows - which leads to butter, cheeses, yoghurt and, of course, milk - and apart from the dairy we have several workshops, the pottery, the granary, farm buildings, the cottage school room, a three-storey manor house, the walled garden, orchard and poly-tunnels. For tentative members we have a series of six fortnights throughout the year - drop us a line, telling us a little about yourself (how interesting, cheerful, hardworking etc you are) if you wish to know more. WWOOF and world visitors - write and we will arrange something. We have lots of mud!

GLANEIRW HOUSING CO-OP

31

THE GUIDE TO
COMMUNAL
LIVING
DIGGERS &
DREAMERS
94/95

Status
existing community

Address
Blaenporth
CARDIGAN
Dyfed
SA43 2HP

Telephone

Number of over 18s
7

Number of under 18s
3

Year started
1975

Situation
rural

Ideological focus
ecological

Open to new members
Yes

Status
existing community

Address
Craigavad
HOLYWOOD
County Down
BT18 0DB

Telephone

Number of over 18s

Number of under 18s

Year started

Situation
rural

Ideological focus
Anthroposophy

Open to new members
Yes

Glencraig Camphill Community is situated on the shores of Belfast Lough and is home for around 180 people living in 15 different households. There is a school for six to nineteen year olds, and a training scheme for young people up to the age of 25 years. It is also home for some adults needing a sheltered environment. Care for the land is an important aspect of the work. Farm and garden are worked bio-dynamically.

A one year orientation course in Anthroposophy (The Science of Man) and Curitive Education is available for those people (19 years and older) who wish to experience life and work with people of special needs in a community. A three year training in Curitive Education is also available.

Training takes place through work, and greater responsibility is given to each person as they show themselves ready. Everyone works co-operatively acknowledging through trust the need for individual initiative and responsibility.

It is a fundamental principle of Camphill that no one receives remuneration directly for the work which is done. Rather each person's needs are met according to individual circumstances. Age, experience and responsibility are not necessarilly relevant to an assessment of their daily needs.

Enquiries by letter or pre-arranged visits are welcome.

This is a monastic community with very strict rules - it is for men only. Submission to spiritual discipline and surrender to one's own real true feelings are an absolute necessity. The monks dress in striped, cotton habits of russet and green ... or in sage green and white striped tunics for casual wear. These are the only colours permitted and are those of Mount Anelog through the seasons. Here, in North Wales, the monks own a tiny smallholding and cottage, Y Graig (The Rock), where they spend some of their time. Most of their work is done at the Monastery in Kentish Town where they make pottery, produce books, paint, do calligraphy and frame pictures. The community wishes to establish a new religion based on Jungian principles ... acknowledging the 'Greater self' with its four-foldness and six pairs of Archetypes corresponding to the six dimensions (this study is called 'Natural Psychology'). The Monastery aims to be the physical manifestation of the purified 'Inner'. The monks live out their own myth by means of 'dream-analysis' and 'receiving'. They rise at 5.00am, have breakfast, have collective housework, building and repairs, then have 'Matins' (service) from 9.00am to 10.00am. After Matins the monks have lunch, a rest, then they all do their own individual work - besides being open to visitors interested in the work of the monastery. Every fortnight there is a 'Sunday Group' for those interested in 'Anelog' work (a derivation of 'Gurdjieff Work') and Natural Psychology'. The latter is the basis of their religion and relates to self-development through art and theatrical expression. There are beautiful masks and puppets emphasising the magical atmosphere of the living rooms, the studio, gallery and 'Salubriat' (shrine room). Decision making starts at breakfast and is based on 'receiving': a process of making feelings conscious. The approach to sexuality is the same and relates to what is usually unconscious. True love and sexuality are not identical. A great deal of attention is paid to a vegetarian diet and most food is cooked or baked in the monastery. The Green Monks buy their food wholesale, dip their own candles and ferment their own altar wine. On Moonday (Monday) elderberry wine and the Moonday Bread, made ritually from twelve ingredients, are shared during a special rite. Interested people can ring between 1.00pm and 8.00pm ... or write (enclosing a stamped addressed envelope). All income and all belongings are shared by the community, but there is a three month trial period for novices who will need to contribute between £30 and £50 a week including any money they earn at the monastery.

GRAIGIAN SOCIETY

33

THE GUIDE TO COMMUNAL **LIVING**
DIGGERS -&- DREAMERS
94/95

Status
existing community

Address
10 Lady Somerset Road
LONDON
NW5 1UP

Telephone
071 485 1646

Number of over 18s
3

Number of under 18s
0

Year started
1983

Situation
urban

Ideological focus
psychological (New Age and Jung)

Open to new members
Yes

GRAIL SOCIETY

 **THE GUIDE TO COMMUNAL LIVING** *DIGGERS & DREAMERS* **94/95**

34

Status
existing community

Address
Waxwell Farm House
125 Waxwell Lane
PINNER
Middlesex
HA5 3ER

Telephone
081 866 21950505

Number of over 18s
24

Number of under 18s

Year started
1932

Situation
suburban

Ideological focus
Christian

Open to new members
Yes

The Grail Community is one of several branches of the Grail Society which was started in Holland in 1921. This is a Roman Catholic Institute of single and married people, men and women, both young and old.

The society seeks, in an increasingly impersonal world, to promote understanding of the uniqueness and value of each person. The long term community, at 'Waxwell', Pinner, consists of women who, choosing to remain single, make a life commitment. Community life involves its members in a close inter-dependent relationship and life-style, sharing all resources and earnings and stressing each person's accountability to the community.

The Grail carries the status of a registered charity. The community home, 'Waxwell' is an Elizabethan farmhouse with library, guest wing and conference extensions set in ten acres of cultivated and wilderness land. The work of the community includes: support for families and married people, publishing, hospitality, residential courses on arts, religion, human growth, focussing on the spiritual, helping those under stress, provision of space and solitude for those seeking rest and prayer.

Short term members and volunteers are welcome. Short term members bring another dimension to community as they share our life for a year or so whilst exploring new directions. They participate fully in the life and work of the community. Volunteers live alongside the community, assisting with the practical chores of the centre and the upkeep of the grounds. In addition to these there are regular participants in spinning and weaving classes, a healing group, prayer and Bible Study groups. People of all religious traditions are welcome.

Grimstone Community was set up to buy and develop the existing successful workshop centre at Grimstone Manor, in the hope of enriching it with the energies of community. We aspire to be a spiritual community or light centre, with one main work or service the provision of a welcoming space for groups and workshops concerned with personal development. This magical spot on the edge of Dartmoor combines natural beauty with a heritage of good practical spiritual work done here in the past! Community commitments include the endeavours (which only partially succeed) to maintain regular meditation and eat at least one meal a day together. We met each week, as a community, alternating a business meeting and a process meeting. Decisions are taken by consensus, with the help of 'positive abstention' from those who disagree with the majority.

Since the Community was formed to buy Grimstone Manor and Mews, plus 27 acres of garden and grazing land, all full members have to invest capital: the normal minimum is £50,000. On joining all members become partners in the business partnership and joint co-owners of the property. All work in the community, from cooking to gardening to cleaning, maintenance or accounts is paid on an equal hourly basis. Two present members work part-time outside, but all members are committed to work for the community on average at least 20 hours per week over the year. Our legal basis is a Trust Deed which lays down who owns what share of the property and defines how to get out. We have no leader or hierarchy, but we do choose 'focalisers' who have overall responsibility for particular areas of work (eg kitchen, menus, ordering, gardening, customer relations). Otherwise the aim is for people to be open to working in as wide a range of jobs as possible. Our diet is mainly vegetarian, but without dogma. We are steadily developing vegetable supplies from our lovely walled garden. We are, in general, flexible, rather than highly structured. We are at present looking for new members but space is limited, it could be difficult to incorporate more facilities without sufficient new investment to enable us to buy or build new property. We are also open to volunteer workers, who work in return for keep, for periods of up to a month. If you are interested in either membership or volunteer work, please contact us first in writing telling us something about yourself.

GRIMSTONE COMMUNITY

35

THE GUIDE TO COMMUNAL LIVING
DIGGERS -&- DREAMERS
94/95

Status
existing community

Address
Grimstone Manor
YELVERTON
Devon
PL20 7QY

Telephone
0822 854358

Number of over 18s
7

Number of under 18s
3

Year started
1990

Situation
rural

Ideological focus
New Age

Open to new members
Yes

GWERIN HOUSING ASSOCIATION

THE GUIDE TO
COMMUNAL
LIVING
DIGGERS
-&-
DREAMERS
36
94/95

Gwerin exists primarily as a housing associ-ation, run as a co-operative and its first aim is to provide accommodation, particularly where there is a strong need that is not being met outside. The only 'capital' required of a new member is a nominal £5 share. Our ideological focus is one of mutual support, through political and religious persuasions may vary quite widely within that framework. Whilst most of our current members seem to be Christian, some with Anthroposophical interests, we are not exclusively religious or non-religious.

Lifestyles within the community are quite varied. Three of our households include individuals who have learning difficulties, whose special needs we hope are met alongside those of other members. They are also family homes in a fairly conventional sense. One of our other two houses is jointly occupied by single people, and the other, Rectory Cottage, is a small family home. This last is separated from the first four (which are neighbours in a terrace of large Victorian town houses sharing a common garden) by about half a mile. In the running of the Association and by a kinship of interests, outlook and ideology, the distance is considerably shortened. The ways of living within Gwerin are as various as the needs of its members, and provided that suitable space is avail-able, we can welcome people from a wide spectrum of prospective new members.

Status
existing community

Address
121 Hagley Road
STOURBRIDGE
West Midlands
DY8 1RD

Telephone
0384 396582

Number of over 18s
20

Number of under 18s
6

Year started
1980

Situation
urban

Ideological focus
co-operative living

Open to new members
Yes

Harmony Community Trust is a small group formed in 1992 with the aim of setting up a residential community in Cornwall. The focus for the community will be to live in harmony with each other, the outside community and our surroundings. By using appropriate technology, conserving resources and utilising the principles of permaculture we believe we can create a sustainable environment offering a high quality of life for a low cash economy. Our ideas on how the project will operate are not yet fully formed. As a guide we would expect the centre to have: small scale engineering and craft workshops, land and rooms to hold events, workshops, celebrations etc. There would also be rooms set aside for meditation, healing, private accommodation for residents and accommodation for visitors.

With the help of the *Devon Co-operative Development Agency* we have registered the project as a company limited by guarantee under articles suitable for a co-operative. We want a non-heirarchical organisation where decisions will be made by meditation and consensus, followed by vote if all else fails. As a group we place particular importance on providing private space for members together with a strong sense of mutual support through contact, hugs and personal development. Laughter and celebration are central to our vision. At the moment we have three active members and no clear idea of how we can bring our vision to reality. To do so we need more people and more capital to buy a property and set up the centre. We would welcome contact from anyone who finds this project interesting. Since it is difficult to anticipate where we will be when this is published initial contact will have to be through *Devon CDA* who will pass on messages and correspondence.

**HARMONY
COMMUNITY
TRUST**

37

THE GUIDE TO
COMMUNAL
LIVING
DIGGERS *&*
DREAMERS
94/95

Status
embryonic community

Address
*care of
Devon CDA
138 North Road East
PLYMOUTH
PL4 6AQ*

Telephone
0752 223481

Number of over 18s

Number of under 18s

Year started

Situation

Ideological focus
harmony

Open to new members
Yes

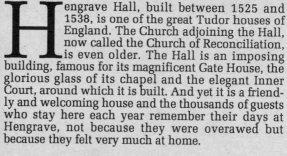

HENGRAVE HALL CENTRE

THE GUIDE TO COMMUNAL LIVING
DIGGERS & DREAMERS
94/95

38

engrave Hall, built between 1525 and 1538, is one of the great Tudor houses of England. The Church adjoining the Hall, now called the Church of Reconciliation, is even older. The Hall is an imposing building, famous for its magnificent Gate House, the glorious glass of its chapel and the elegant Inner Court, around which it is built. And yet it is a friendly and welcoming house and the thousands of guests who stay here each year remember their days at Hengrave, not because they were overawed but because they felt very much at home.

For most of its history Hengrave Hall was a family home. Since 1974 it has served as a Centre for groups holding conferences and for individuals looking for a day or two's 'peace and quiet'. The Centre is run by a Community of Christians from different Church traditions. The Community includes a group of Roman Catholic sisters, members of the Congregation of the Assumption, who are the present owners of the Hall. The Community aims to serve all the Churches through the Centre, to further understanding between Christians and those of other faiths, and to work for reconciliation between individuals and in society at large. All are welcome to join in with any part of the Community's worship.

Status
existing community

Address
Bury St Edmunds
Suffolk
IP28 6LZ

Telephone
0284 701561

Number of over 18s
20

Number of under 18s

Year started
1974

Situation
rural

Ideological focus
Christian ecumenical

Open to new members
Yes

W e are an ecumenical Christian community seeking radical new ways of living the gospel in today's world. Our founder, George MacLeod, now the Very Reverend Lord MacLeod of Fuinary, started the movement in the 1930s because he felt the church at that time had no message for the unemployed living in tenements and back streets in his parish in Govan, Glasgow. He set out to make the church relevant to the needs of the working class and to apply on weekdays what was sung about on Sundays. The ruined Benedictine Abbey on Iona was restored with teams of craftsmen and trainee ministers, and today is the home of the Iona Community.

Guests come to stay at the Abbey or at the MacLeod Centre, the newly built centre for reconciliation (for programmed weeks during the summer season or for open weeks in the spring and autumn). Members live all over Britain and the world and follow a five fold rule of economic sharing, prayer and bible reading, sharing and use of time, actions for peace and justice in society, and meeting with accounting to each other. The island centres are run by staff staying for one to three years and teams of volunteers who work for six to twelve weeks during the summer season. Celtic spirituality forms the basis of the ecumenical worship and we follow George MacLeod's vision that work, worship and recreation are all equally important and indivisible. To become a member of the community, one should contact the Associates Secretary at: Iona Community, Pearce Institute, Govan, Glasgow G51 3UU

IONA COMMUNITY

39

THE GUIDE TO COMMUNAL LIVING

DIGGERS & DREAMERS

94/95

Status
existing community

Address
The Abbey
Isle of Iona
Argyll
PA76 6SN

Telephone

Number of over 18s

Number of under 18s

Year started
1938

Situation
rural

Ideological focus
Christian

Open to new members
Yes

KEVERAL FARM COMMUNITY

Status
existing community

Address
Keveral Farm
near Seaton
LOOE
Cornwall
PL13 1PA

Telephone
05035 215

Number of over 18s
10

Number of under 18s
3

Year started
1973

Situation
rural

Ideological focus
mixed

Open to new members
Yes

Keveral Farm is managed by two Co-operatives: One Community, which is a Housing Co-op, and Keveral Farmers, a Worker's Co-op. Permanent residents are members of both, and weekly meetings are an essential feature. Fortunately, these are no longer the six-hour hostile epics that they once were (the calm before the next storm?). Maintaining the house and buildings and working the land provides the main focus of our work here, as well as shaping our own lives in our own desired ways - we like to be flexible enough to give members the freedom to develop their own personal projects. However, we often find ourselves working separately rather than co-operatively.

We are also developing the educational potential of Keveral, through Kids' Camps and a Visitors' Centre. We would like to help the world become a better place, as well as offering people a sanctuary from Babylon. We are in a beautiful location a short walk from the South Cornwall coast, and usually have a caravan available for short retreats and holidays, as well as a camping field. We recognise the importance of a broad "shared vision" as a unifying factor but without a tight entry system, members are here for many different personal reasons, and we each need to be aware of these. Hence, we try to cater for everyone's needs and wishes, without imposing a rigid structure. The stated objectives of the Worker's Co-op are: To operate an organic farm, combined with recreational and educational facilities. To encourage members to operate independent co-operative activities with similar aims!We rely heavily on state support for organic agriculture, nature conservation, housing co-ops, and child-rearing, though some of us are self-employed from time to time. We are looking into farm diversification ideas to provide incomes from he farm. We have livery stables and a forge running as independent businesses. We are into permaculture, trees, horses, good food, home-made alcohol, living under canvas, fires, music, kids, watching television and having fun. We sometimes even socialise together, especially at the Breakwater and the Smugglers. We hope that Keveral will help inspire people to change and improve their lives and to create alternatives everywhere. Prospective members should share our broad aims, be enthusiastic about community life on the Farm, and get to know us over a period of time before asking to become a member. We welcome visitors, volunteers, hikers, cyclists, builders, growers and sweeper-uppers - but not all at once, and contact us first please.

The Laurels is a 100 year old building which used to be a Doctor's surgery. It was converted into a housing co-op in 1982. The house is now owned by Milton Keynes Borough Council who rent it out to us as a co-op. There are eight private rooms, shared kitchen, living room, TV room, workshop and a big garden where we grow vegetables and keep chickens. There are now eight adults and four kids living here.

We pay the neighbouring Rainbow Housing Co-op for the use of some of their facilities. Our members are expected to do their share in the running of the co-op. This includes maintenance, gardening and book-keeping as well as participation at our monthly meetings and a general interest in a communal and co-operative lifestyle. We elect annually a treasurer and a secretary. Most decisions are made by consensus. We decide on new members by inviting them to visit and get to know us. Most of us are vegetarians.

LAURELS
HOUSING
CO-OP

41

THE GUIDE TO
COMMUNAL
LIVING
DIGGERS & DREAMERS

94/95

Status
existing community

Address
64 High Street
New Bradwell
MILTON KEYNES
Buckinghamshire
MK13 0BP

Telephone
0908 225769

Number of over 18s
8

Number of under 18s
4

Year started
1982

Situation
urban

Ideological focus
co-operation

Open to new members
Yes

LAURIESTON HALL

THE GUIDE TO COMMUNAL **LIVING**

DIGGERS-&-DREAMERS

94/95

42

Status
existing community

Address
*Laurieston
CASTLE DOUGLAS
Kirkcudbrightshire
DG7 2NB*

Telephone

Number of over 18s
24

Number of under 18s
8

Year started
1972

Situation
rural

Ideological focus
no one word!

Open to new members
Yes

About half of us live in the main house, mostly in small groups sharing one of the three communal kitchens, and half live in cottages or caravans. Although each adult or family is domestically and financially independent, we work and play together, and some of us would say that the line between the two is often blurred. The day to day running of various work areas is largely done by people taking responsibility for what they see needs doing. The major areas - garden, wood, maintenance, dairy, finance, land - are managed by 'committees' which meet regularly.

Our 'play' ranges from creating pantomimes, through dance and music (there is a resident international folk music band), to cricket and bridge. The *People Centre* is run, with help from other co-op members, by a small group of us. It's financially separate from the housing co-op, and organises events and workshops for groups of 15 to 75 people from spring to autumn. At the end of 1992, our numbers having increased substantially over the previous two years, we took a decision not to look for new members. This was to allow us an (indefinite) period of consolidation, and time to review our structures and systems, some of which needed adapting to our new size. Visitors are still welcome and we value their contribution to the community. Visitor Weeks (except for personal guests we're not able to invite people at other times) are at the same time as our Community Work Weeks (usually three each year) and visitors join in with buildings maintenance, gardening, land work and domestic work - we function as one communal group at these times.

Architect's drawing of Laurieston Hall, 1893

L ifespan is a workers' and housing co-operative. We live in two terraces of old railway workers' houses on the edge of the Yorkshire Pennines. Everyone who lives here has their own room and all other space is shared. We all participate in the running of our print business which is housed on the premises, publishing our own booklets and calendar as well as commercial printing. This provides most of our income which we share; no money is needed to join us.

Child care is shared although this is to a lesser extent than in the past. We eat together - vegetarian and vegan food. We produce some of our own food organically in our three quarter acre garden and in our greenhouse and poly tunnel. We also keep a few hens. The houses were built in 1908 and some are still awaiting modernisation. We have an on-going programme of building and maintenance work in order to improve the property with both large and small scale projects on our houses and workshops. We are almost always looking for enthusiastic and energetic new members - empathy with what we are trying to do and the ability to fit in socially with the existing group are what is important. If you would like to visit, please write to us (enclosing a stamped addressed envelope or international reply coupon) suggesting when you could come, initially for a couple of days, and we'll get back to you and let you know if this time is alright. We'll also send you our Introductory Booklet which should answer most of your questions about visiting us. We look forward to meeting you.

LIFESPAN COMMUNITY

43

THE GUIDE TO COMMUNAL **LIVING**
DIGGERS & DREAMERS
94/95

Status
existing community

Address
Townhead
Dunford Bridge
SHEFFIELD
S30 6TG

Telephone
0226 762359

Number of over 18s
8

Number of under 18s
4

Year started
1974

Situation
moorland

Ideological focus
indescribable

Open to new members
Yes

LITTLE GROVE COMMUNITY

THE GUIDE TO
COMMUNAL
LIVING

DIGGERS &
DREAMERS

94/95

44

L ittle Grove was established in 1983 and typically has about twelve members. At present, they are all adults, aged from 27 to 70 years and about 50%:50% men and women. We are broadly "alternative" in outlook and values, but have no common ideology beyond that. We are all pretty actively involved in the world, with a wide variety of jobs. About half of us work partly or wholly from home: there is plenty of space for offices, studios and workshops, plus a thriving education centre. Some of us use the latter to run a programme of personal development courses and it is also used extensively by visiting groups.

There are five acres of gardens and fields. Each member has a room or two of their own and we share bathrooms (several), kitchens, lounge, hall, television room, laundry and more. Most main meals are eaten together. House business meetings are held fortnightly and there is a monthly meeting to deal with other matters. Little Grove is in a very quiet rural setting, but close to several towns and about an hour from London. Please send a 40pin stamps for full details.

Status
existing community

Address
Grove Lane
Orchard Leigh
CHESHAM
Buckinghamshire
HP5 3QL

Telephone
0494 782720

Number of over 18s
14

Number of under 18s
0

Year started
1983

Situation
rural

Ideological focus
various

Open to new members
Yes

othlorien was established in 1978. It consists of a large log house with 14 bedrooms and communal living areas. It is set in seventeen acres of grounds which include organic vegetable gardens, woodland, workshops and outbuildings. In 1989, *Rokpa Trust*, which has grown out of Samye Ling Tibetan Buddhist Centre took over the running of Lothlorien. Its aim is to maintain a supportive community in Lothlorien, where those who suffer from mental health problems can grow and develop through participation in community life. The guiding principles of the community are hospitality, care and respect for the person, and a belief that the potential of the individual can be encouraged through a communal life in which all have a contribution to make.

There are places for four live-in volunteers who play a key role in helping to create a warm, accepting atmosphere in the community. Lothlorien now employs a manager, support worker and garden co-ordinator who provide a continuity of support to the community. We have vacancies on a regular basis as we see Lothlorien as a place where people can grow and develop for a period of time (usually up to one year). People are then encouraged to move on rather than seeing Lothlorien as their long term home. Please contact the manager by phone or letter if you have any queries.

LOTHLORIEN COMMUNITY

45

THE GUIDE TO COMMUNAL LIVING
DIGGERS -&- DREAMERS
94/95

Status
existing community

Address
Corsock
CASTLE DOUGLAS
Kirkcudbrightshire
DG7 3DR

Telephone
06444 602

Number of over 18s
14

Number of under 18s

Year started
1978

Situation
rural

Ideological focus
individual well being

Open to new members
Yes

LOWER SHAW FARM

THE GUIDE TO
COMMUNAL
LIVING
DIGGERS &
DREAMERS

94/95

46

The community, comprising three families, lives in a 200 year old listed farmhouse. Each family has its own living space but kitchen, bathrooms etc are shared. To earn a living the community runs a business in the farm's outbuildings, converted to meeting rooms and dormitaries, for up to 40 visitors.

The business is weekend and week-long courses, educational and recreational, in a range of alternative traditional and conventional activities (send a stamped addressed envelope for complete details). The farm (ex-dairy) is on the outskirts of Swindon and has goats, poultry, peacocks, a large organically run (and permaculture based) fruit and vegetable garden, a kindergarten, lots of local links, a national and international network of friends and supporters, regular meetings to ensure continuity and good order and a sense of humour. If you want to know more then write with a stamped addressed envelope.

Status
existing community

Address
Old Shaw Lane
Shaw
SWINDON
Wiltshire
SN5 9PJ

Telephone
0793 771080

Number of over 18s
6

Number of under 18s
7

Year started
1975

Situation
urban

Ideological focus
humanist/ecological

Open to new members
Yes

This is a long-standing community. Yet anyone looking, primarily, for a good community to live in is liable to be disappointed. Our main reason for being together is spiritual. What we do is very much of secondary importance to how we do it. We are part of a worldwide network known as "The Emissaries", with sister-communities in many countries. We are the main Emissary community in Britain. Three times a week we meet for an hour or more to consider in depth our current experience of life. We also make regular use of a technique for spiritual "attunement". The focal point of our week is the meeting held at 11.00am every Sunday, which is always open to the public. Living in a community is not essential to our approach to life, but it is useful because it intensifies the pressure for change. Although there is a high level of love and fulfilment among us, this is also frequently a very uncomfortable place to be: the recipe only works if we are committed to maintaining, as far as we are able, a consistent sense of vision, purpose and stable atmosphere. Emissaries share a strong respect for individual integrity and perception. Our diets, for example, range from omnivorous to vegan with many variations. In finances, each person is responsible for their own income and basic expenses, and for deciding what they donate to the community. Communal decisions are made in many and varied ways. The management of our affairs emerges from a core of agreement. We all accept responsibility for generating that core. We are not farmers, or even substantial vegetable-growers: our central home, Mickleton House, is right in the middle of a Cotswald village with a population of 1,500 or more. Some of us live in our own homes, up to eight miles away. We work in a wide variety of jobs in the neighbourhood - including some employed in Mickleton House to serve the community. As well as our Sunday meetings, we welcome visitors at other times. We do ask that visitors make a donation for their meals and board, and anyone planning to visit should let us know in advance. We are not usually able to offer "keep in exchange for work". People who eventually make their home here normally do so after quite a long period of friendship and association with what we stand for. Courses of varying length are offered over the year; through them anyone may experience our approach to spiritual education. If you feel drawn to our approach, please write to us, saying when you would like to come and giving some detail about yourself. In particular, you should say what it is that attracts you. If you know someone already connected with us, let us know who it is.

MICKLETON EMMISARY COMMUNITY

47

THE GUIDE TO COMMUNAL **LIVING** DIGGERS -&- DREAMERS

94/95

Status
existing community

Address
Mickleton House
MICKLETON
Gloucestershire
GL55 6RY

Telephone
0386 438251/438308

Number of over 18s
45

Number of under 18s
9

Year started
1980

Situation
village

Ideological focus
spiritual

Open to new members
Yes

MONIMAIL TOWER PROJECT

THE GUIDE TO
COMMUNAL
LIVING

DIGGERS &
DREAMERS

48

94/95

Status
existing community

Address
Letham
by CUPAR
Fife
KY7 7RJ

Telephone
033 781420

Number of over 18s
11

Number of under 18s

Year started
1985

Situation
rural

Ideological focus
lifestyle

Open to new members
Yes

Monimail was once the palace of Cardinal Beaton before it was dismantled to build the Melville estate. The Victorians built extensive walls and a terrace. The grounds were left to their own devices as the Melville estate was divided up. The Tower has survived all this although is now in some need of repair. In 1985 a community was started and temporary buildings were erected. None of the pioneering members lives here now, although some are still involved as trustees.

We are a relatively new group, and are in the process of continuing projects already set in motion, such as the restoration of the Tower, whilst implementing our own projects, such as building more permanent accommodation. We have started with a Walter Segal low energy house. We try to share as much as possible, from cooking, cleaning and working to transport, skills and resources. We eat mostly a vegetarian diet with allowances for other preferences. The main areas of work are the garden, the woods, building and administration. We pay rent to the Project and do not share personal income - we would like to find more ways for the Project to become self-supporting. We also like to meet people, play music, dance and generally have fun. We have weekly meetings and make our decisions by consensus. At present we operate as an educational charity. Our aims are to build a resource for ourselves and other people with which to learn how to live together in a way that is beneficial to all. At the moment we have no children living here, but some visit regularly - we are open to people in different situations and the ideas that they bring. For more information or to arrange a visit please write to us, if possible enclosing a stamped addressed envelope.

In the beautiful soft rolling hills of a Dorset valley, three miles from the sea, we are a registered charity with an educational focus operating a business hosting both holistic and educational groups. We live in a large Victorian neo-gothic house, an ex-vicarage and outbuildings. We are at present three families, one couple and individuals, who have their own room, sometimes children too. The visiting groups, 2,000 people per year, provide our income and pocket money. We are an intentional community and try to treat each person as individual and unique, in relation to our needs and the needs of the community (maintenance help is often welcome!).

We attune at 9.15am, eat lunch at 1.00pm, supper at 6.00pm and our weekly meeting operates towards consensus so that we clearly slow down. The children go to the local schools and we run a toddler group 0-3 years and a Steiner based playgroup 3-5 years for our kids and the local children. We have a pottery, woodwork shed, and art room always available for use. Regularly we have creative dance classes, circle dancing, basket weaving, batik and drumming workshops. We have 12 acres of land, a one-acre, organic, south-facing walled garden that produces most of our vegetables from late spring, and some fruit. From our three milking cows we make yoghurt and cheese. Telephone or write for our brochure. A good way to visit Monkton Wyld is to come on a visitor week, which we have once a month (we have 150 membership enquiries a year plus masses of volunteer requests) or write about yourself, what interests you and what you have to offer.

MONKTON WYLD COURT

49

THE GUIDE TO
COMMUNAL
LIVING
DIGGERS & DREAMERS
94/95

Status
existing community

Address
Monkton Wyld
Charmouth
BRIDPORT
Dorset
DT6 6DQ

Telephone
0297 60342

Number of over 18s
15

Number of under 18s
7

Year started
1982

Situation
rural

Ideological focus
holistic education

Open to new members
Yes

MORNING-TON GROVE COMMUNITY

In 1982 two large houses in Bow were bought by a group of people, some of whom had lived in a sister community in Bethnal Green. Now we are a very mixed community of 14 people (plus guests) living in two beautiful Victorian houses with a large garden, in a densely populated part of East London. The community has a certain amount of structure. We organise mainly through fortnightly meetings where consensus decisions are made. These are either "business" meetings to discuss issues like rent, food, finances, repairs etc. "Relationship" meetings are very variable meetings. They range from working on relationship difficulties, to a time for people to 'share things'. Each house has meetings to discuss the practicalities of day to day living.

We have a unique rent system. We work out the community's expenditure and from this decide an average rent to cover costs. Each individual then decides how much they feel they can afford. If the total sum from everyone's rent is what we need *wonderful*, if not we enter into a process of negotiation. So far we have never needed to do this. The ideological focus of the community is difficult to define. People are interested in ecology, therapy, the peace movement, music etc. The twelve adults here at the time of writing include teachers, therapists, a lawyer, a social worker, a musician, and a graphic designer. There are also currently two lively children aged 11 and 14. We describe ourselves as a vegetarian community although not all members are vegetarians. We buy most food in bulk (organic if possible) and we also have a garden. We are often full but we welcome people to visit and enquire about the future

THE GUIDE TO COMMUNAL LIVING

DIGGERS-&-DREAMERS

94/95

50

Status
existing community

Address
13-14 Mornington Grove
Bow
LONDON
E3 4NS

Telephone

Number of over 18s
12

Number of under 18s
2

Year started
1982

Situation
urban

Ideological focus
mixed

Open to new members
Yes

The New Creation Christian Community consists of 60 plus houses in various locations around England. Most of the houses are in Central England, but there are a scattering further afield: Hastings, Shepton Mallet, Liverpool, Sheffield and Great Yarmouth. The Community is a major part of the *Jesus Fellowship Church*, well-known to many for its *Jesus Army* outreach activity. Theologically, we're Reformed, Evangelical and Charismatic, and support all the historic Christian creeds and doctrines. Our all-things-in-common lifestyle is inspired by that adopted by the Christians in Jerusalem in the first days of the church.

All of us have experienced the life-changing power of God through faith in Jesus, and we want to live out this new life in a new way that shows the love and life of God. Our backgrounds are varied; some are (very) rough, others more respectable. As long as you are in sympathy with our aims and willing to participate in our daily activities and worship, you're welcome to visit us for a short or a long stay. Hospitality is freely provided for short stays, and there is a low charge made for longer visits, though we won't turn you away just because you can't pay! Our Central Office (ring or write) will put you in touch with local Community households.

NEW CREATION CHRISTIAN COMMUNITY

51

THE GUIDE TO COMMUNAL LIVING
DIGGERS & DREAMERS
94/95

Status
network

Address
New Creation
Farmhouse
Nether Heyford
NORTHAMPTON
NN7 3LB

Telephone
0327 349991

Number of over 18s
550

Number of under 18s
250

Year started
1974

Situation
rural and urban

Ideological focus
Christian

Open to new members
Yes

NEWBOLD HOUSE

I n a rural setting a 100 year old Victorian house is home to an intentional community where we explore creative ways of living and working together in harmony with each other and our environment. Our purpose as a spiritual and educational centre is fulfilled in several ways: we run a variety of spiritual and personal growth workshops, short term guest programmes and long term guest programmes (three months).

We are part of the Findhorn Community but independent of the *Findhorn Foundation* and are committed to bring about the highest ideals of the Findhorn Foundation in our own unique way, becoming yet another expression of the same spirit.

We have a diverse approach to spirit in our membership. Our structures are quite formal and tend to follow the general pattern of the Findhorn Foundation. All our money dealings are done by attunement, eg no set allowances for members, each member attuning to their needs, each member attuning to the community in terms of an entrance fee. Decisions are made on a consensus basis only. There are two formal channels for dealing with relationships - family meetings and members' meetings. There is a general openness to exploring ways of keeping all relationships clear between all members.

We have a large garden but the emphasis in the garden is education rather than self sufficiency. Our diet is vegetarian. Work includes maintaining the grounds, gardens, education programs and the general running of a centre such as reception, cooking etc. We have six acres of land and each member has their own living space. We are very willing to respond to enquiries. All prospective members are required to participate in the three month guest program before considering membership.

Status
existing community

Address
St Leonards Road
FORRES
Grampian
IV36 0RE

Telephone
0309 672659

Number of over 18s
7

Number of under 18s
0

Year started
1979

Situation
rural

Ideological focus
spiritual

Open to new members
Yes

Our School Community is never static. Being a member of the *Association of Camphill Communities* we are known internationally, but more often through personal contacts, ie by recommendation of former "co-workers". Some eight to twelve people join us usually in summer for a year or longer. As a Steiner Special School we want people with some training in this field but at least people who are motivated and have the ability to get on with special children and with their fellow co-workers. We give an introduction in the first week and a follow up throughout the year.

The seven acres of Ochil Tower are just off the High Street in the small town of Auchterarder between Perth and Stirling with a splendid view of the Ochil Hills. Park, gardens, orchards, a donkey field and playgrounds form the pleasant environment of the community. We have an open door policy with parents and visitors coming frequently. The children are accommodated in three buildings together with their "grown ups" and there are two additional houses with accommodation as well as two school buildings (with hall and stage).

The practical day to day care and work is varied, demanding and enjoyable too. The time table is structured. Group meetings and discussions bring about the strong sense of therapeutic community. Here common decisions are made. Whilst being here everyone is expected to join in to the full and has in return all the communal benefits and pocket money. Though no one is obliged to accept our philosophy personally - it is the working basis of our community. A rich cultural life is being fostered with music, country dancing, eurythmy, drama - with and for children. We grow much of our own organic and bio-dynamic vegetables and fruit. We share meals with the children. Co-workers have their own room. There is one day off and a relaxed weekend fortnightly. Of the fourteen weeks of school holidays, half is spent at the school with many necessary and leisure activities. The school is a limited company without share capital and a charity. Inquiries by letter or visit are welcome.

OCHIL TOWER

53

THE GUIDE TO COMMUNAL LIVING

DIGGERS & DREAMERS

94/95

Status
existing community

Address
Aucterarder
Perthshire
PH3 1AD

Telephone
0764 662416

Number of over 18s
25

Number of under 18s
35

Year started
1972

Situation
rural

Ideological focus
Anthroposophy

Open to new members
Yes

OLD HALL COMMUNITY

THE GUIDE TO COMMUNAL **LIVING**
DIGGERS &- DREAMERS
94/95

54

Status
existing community

Address
East Bergholt
COLCHESTER
Essex
CO7 6TG

Telephone
0206 298294

Number of over 18s
41

Number of under 18s
17

Year started
1974

Situation
rural

Ideological focus
Green

Open to new members
Yes

1994 is our 20th birthday. We are a group of families and individuals who have chosen to live together. Many of the founder members are stille here and, although people come and go, we are a fairly settled community. We are located in the heart of picturesque Constable country on the edge of a large village . There is no single purpose for living at Old Hall. Generally however, we share a concern for the environment and a desire to live a co-operative, healthy and self-sufficient lifestyle. We see ourselves as part of the wider community rather than separated from it - our children generally attend local schools and many people have jobs locally. Old Hall was originally a manor, then a convent, and latterly a Franciscan friary. The building covers about two acres of ground. Many facilities are shared - these include a large kitchen/dining area, sitting room, sewing room, ballroom, library, washrooms, showers and laundry room. Some of the many buildings have been converted to workspaces. When members join the community, they purchase loan stock in the Housing Association which entitles them to private living space and a share in the communal facilities and land. Unit sizes vary but a full-size unit is roughly the size of a family house. We own 70 acres, cultivated organically. We have vegetable gardens, orchards, woodlands, soft fruit patches, and a large lawn and play area, plus pastures and arable farmland. We grow wheat, potatoes and other crops for animal fodder. We are largely self-sufficient in meat and vegetables, although we do buy in other foodstuffs. We have sheep, dairy cows, chickens, geese, ducks, bees, cats and ponies. Decisions are reached by consensus at a weekly meeting. Each year we elect a committee and in addition we have convenors for the land, domestic matters, energy and building maintenance. These sub-groups have regular meetings and make recommendations to the weekly meeting. Members are expected to work 12-15 hours/week. Domestic work is done via a voluntary rota system. A certain amount of commitment, drive and stamina is necessary for happy co-existence. Most social activities are informal and spontaneous but we have big parties and sometimes hold events open to the public. Christmas, New Year and our summer birthday are celebrated in grand style. Living in a large group of people has its joys - and its difficulties. Not everyone gets on all the time and decisions can be frustratingly hard to reach. However, on the whole we are a bit like an extended family. Despite the number of people, it is always possible to find peace and quiet. People interested in joining should write to the Applicant Secretary.

Parsonage Farm is a community of nine adults and five children about twelve miles from Cambridge. We live in a large old house in three and a half acres of land at the edge of a large village. Most people have absorbing jobs outside the community so the main activity that brings us together is caring for the large organic vegetable garden that supplies most of our vegetarian diet (with occasional fish!). Every third weekend or so we work together with *WWOOF*ers on the garden and we commit ourselves to one week a year of house maintenance. The community has a large Elizabethan barn where there is workshop space and the potential for development of other ideas. We eat together in the evening and support each other informally in childcare and life.

The group is quite stable; the most recent member joined over four years ago and some members have been here over eighteen years. Some people here work in *Delta T Devices*, a co-operative business producing electronic research instruments. *Delta T* was formed by community members twenty years ago and is still going strong; employing twenty-six at the last count. We are a varied group with interests ranging from re-evaluation counselling to sea canoeing to African drumming and dancing. We like to relax together particularly in the summer when barbecues and trips to swim in the local brick pit (and cover ourselves in clay!) is a regular feature. At the moment we are full but may have places in the future. We encourage people who want to visit us to write and visit on a gardening weekend.

PARSONAGE FARM

55

THE GUIDE TO
COMMUNAL
LIVING
DIGGERS &
DREAMERS
94/95

Status
existing community

Address
128 Low Road
Burwell
Cambridgeshire
CB5 0EJ

Telephone

Number of over 18s
9

Number of under 18s
5

Year started
1971

Situation
rural

Ideological focus
unfocussed

Open to new members
No

PENNINE CAMPHILL COMMUNITY

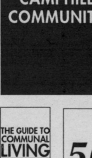
Status
existing community

Address
Boyne Hill House
Chapelthorpe
WAKEFIELD
West Yorkshire
WF4 3JH

Telephone
0924 254054

Number of over 18s
55

Number of under 18s
19

Year started
1977

Situation
semi-rural

Ideological focus
Anthroposophy

Open to new members
Yes

The community supports a college for those with special needs. Twenty-two co-workers and their families live and work with 43 students. The students are of both sexes and aged between 16 and 23. The course at Pennine aims to guide and help the student group through adolescence in a therapeutic environment. The student group has considerable abilities but mental, social, or emotional difficulties. Each of the four households are run on an extended family basis with shared mealtimes and common areas. The students live in the community during term time and attend classes or participate in the workshops and working life. The co-workers all work on a voluntary basis receiving no wage or salary but their daily needs are met by the community.

There is always an international flavour to the community with usually half the co-workers coming from other countries. A small farm and vegetable gardens are worked bio-dynamically and provide much of the Community's needs. There are several craft workshops including a woodworkshop, pottery, weaving and basket workshop, with facilities for other crafts. A college building houses classrooms, a bakery and a hall in which plays, folk dancing, and festive occasions are celebrated. We are always open to enquiries, our usual request is that a potential co-worker has a year free of commitments and would be prepared to live, work and learn alongside others in the community.

The Earth is a living and self regulating being. Irresponsible activities of the human race threaten its ability to sustain life. It is our responsibility to care for the land and be good stewards to ensure healthy living for all, now and in the future. So starts our 'Declaration of Trust' a set of ideals, and a proposed plan to initiate the removal of land from the marketplace. The idea is that we put 2% of our incomes (some of us have been doing so for five or six years) into a fund to purchase land. Once bought it is held in trust forever, with access to all (including wildlife), but 'looked after' (the main foreseeable threat being destructive humans) by a stewardship group.

We envisage that we will buy our first plot of land in the near future, perhaps before this piece is published. At present we have meetings four times a year, where we get to know each other, discuss ideas for the future, and find common ground and ideals through consensus. Individual living arrangements on future plots of land will be up to the stewards who will live on it and the specific land. We hope others, who appreciate the damaging effect of 'ownership' of the Earth, will join us, and as our group grows it will divide and create smaller groups to go on and grow and divide.We are eager to hear from prospective new members and produce a newsletter.

PEOPLES LAND GROUP

57

THE GUIDE TO COMMUNAL **LIVING**
DIGGERS -&- DREAMERS
94/95

Status
embryonic community

Address
care of Diggers and Dreamers

Telephone

Number of over 18s
30

Number of under 18s

Year started

Situation

Ideological focus
ecological

Open to new members
Yes

PLANTS FOR A FUTURE

 58

94/95

THE GUIDE TO COMMUNAL LIVING

DIGGERS &- DREAMERS

Status
existing community

Address
The Field
Higher Penpol
St Veep
LOSTWITHIEL
Cornwall
PL22 0NC

Telephone
0208 873554/873623

Number of over 18s
5

Number of under 18s

Year started
1990

Situation
rural

Ideological focus
ecological

Open to new members
Yes

We are a small group of people in the early stages of setting up a village-style community which will allow the extent of privacy which the individual desires. This can range from an individual house to a shared communal house within the village. So far we have 32 acres of land but cannot live on it. We live in rented and shared accommodation in a village about two miles from the land. The main focus of the community will be to support the workers' co-op that promotes the aims of Plants for a Future. These aims are based on the belief that plants can provide us with the vast majority of our daily needs without the need to use animals either for food or for any other commodity. We have information on over 6,000 species of plants that can be grown outdoors in Britain and can provide us with food, fuel, fibre for clothes etc, medicines, building materials and so much more. We are also growing about 1,800 of these species. The community, as it develops, will be involved in growing the plants, experimenting with them, learning how to utilize them and making both plants and information available to anyone who is interested. We do have structures but try to be as informal as possible. Our ultimate aim is to go beyond the money-based economy. To this extent we are all involved in a workers' co-op where, when it becomes viable, there will be full income sharing. We prefer to barter with outside groups - we do not have set prices for the plants that we supply but instead invite donations. We do not have an internal economy preferring to work for the benefit of the community rather than for our pocket. All decision making is by consensus if at all possible. However, if after a set period no decision can be reached we do resort to a vote. We are at an early stage in our development, both social and practical. We want to develop closer bonds between ourselves and try to have various communal events such as music, yoga and circle dancing in order to strengthen these ties. There are no children in the community as yet, we would hope to educate them ourselves as and when they come along. We welcome vistors, either for the day or longer stays, and are looking for new members. These people do not need any special skills but would need to be able to commit themselves to the project and be willing to learn. All visitors should contact us in advance, particularly if you would like to stay for a night or more since space is very limited. We do also encourage visitors to put in some work with us when they visit. If we spend some of our time showing you what we are doing it is nice if you can spend some time helping us.

Post Green Community takes its inspiration from the Christian gospel. Its members seek to become more whole people, better able to reflect the life of Jesus in the various services they offer to people in need in the Poole area and beyond. Their work is organised through two charities (*Post Green Community Trust* and *East Holton Charity*). Community members live in several houses in the Lytchett Minster area, some singly, some as extended families. Two 'novice' members who live on a housing estate north of Poole are evaluating their calling to be part of the community.

Post Green Community's vision is to create an environment which facilitates healing. We offer residential care, counselling, spiritual direction and a wide variety of courses exploring spiritual, psychological and theological issues of importance for the 1990s, based on an extensive ministry over the past 25 years. We are helping found a new residential Centre for people with disabilities and carers called Holton Lee, which will offer hands-on experience of the natural environment, workshops, therapy and training in self-development. We are actively fund raising for this centre, which is due for completion in 1995. It will be located in a beautiful area near the shores of Poole Harbour, and is associated with a heathland regeneration scheme and wider conservation management goals, to which it will contribute over the years ahead. Holton Lee will offer a unique and much needed resource both to carers and people with a wide variety of handicaps.

We also support the Broken Wall Community in Capetown. This group (coloured, black and white) seek by their shared lifestyle and commitment to non-violence to be an example of post-apartheid multi-cultural co-operation in South Africa. They have fostered the development of a number of crêches for young children and night shelters for the homeless in the black townships. They also offer a home to a number of black students who otherwise would not have the resources to study for university entrance examinations, and they work to raise the awareness in South African churches of the racism that is prevalent among them. Post Green collects funds in the UK for the support of this pioneering community. Approaches to Post Green Community about visits or membership can be made by post (care of *Diggers and Dreamers*).

POST GREEN COMMUNITY

THE GUIDE TO COMMUNAL **LIVING**
DIGGERS *&* DREAMERS
94/95

Status
existing community

Address
care of Diggers and Dreamers

Telephone

Number of over 18s
15

Number of under 18s
4

Year started
1974

Situation
rural

Ideological focus
Christian

Open to new members
Yes

POSTLIP HALL

60

Status
existing community

Address
Winchcombe
near CHELTENHAM
Gloucestershire
GL54 5AQ

Telephone

Number of over 18s
16

Number of under 18s
13

Year started
1970

Situation
rural

Ideological focus
mixed

Open to new members
Yes

We are a group of eight families who live together, in self-contained units in Postlip Hall, a large, beautiful, Jacobean manor house with fourteen acres of land in the Cotswolds, seven miles north-east of Cheltenham. Each family owns the leasehold on its individual unit, we all own the free-hold communally. Some parts of the main Hall and outbuildings, the fourteenth century Tithe Barn and the grounds are shared. The upkeep of the grounds, which include gardens, lawns, woodland, grazing for animals and a two-acre, walled, organic vegetable garden, and maintenance work on the Hall and Barn takes up a lot of our time.

We come close to being self-sufficient in vegetables which, with the invaluable aid of *WWOOF*ers, are communally grown. Pigs, sheep, chickens, geese, ducks, rabbits, hamsters, cats and a Shetland pony are looked after by individuals or groups of members. Public events of all kinds are held in the Hall, Barn and grounds. The *Cotswold Beer Festival* is held here annually. From May to September the Barn and Hall are used for arts and craft exhibitions and sales, drama, concerts, weddings, parties, feasts, folk festivals and barn dances. Apart from the enjoyment, the events form a valuable source of income which helps to pay for the upkeep of the buildings and grounds which includes long-term restoration work on the listed Hall and Tithe Barn.

Decisions are made at the monthly Housing Association meetings or in more informal discussions between members. We are a small community, but not a commune. Most of the adults earn their living outside Postlip and although we enjoy eating together two or three times a month, we live independent family lives. What draws us together is being with other people, joining in what the group decides to do for fun, profit or necessity, sharing our needs as and when necessary and just being at Postlip! You are welcome to visit but please arrange a convenient date with us first.

Our building was a Water Board office which we have converted. The families have separate 'units' and most individuals have large bedsits. We have a communal kitchen/dining room, sitting room and facilities for disabled people on the ground floor. We have a Quaker meeting room, and have Quaker meetings for worship at 7.30 am and 9.30 pm daily for half an hour, and also for one hour on Sunday at 10.30am. We have no hierarchy and our decision making is on Quaker lines. Child care is the responsibility of the parents, but as with any extended family it is frequently shared.

School age children attend local schools. We are not income sharing and have no entry fee. Many people have loaned capital and we have a housing co-operative mortgage. Almost everyone has some part-time paid employment outside the community. We are teachers, a potter, a home-help, doctors, a care worker, an occupational therapist, a child minder, a trainee countryside warden and a neighbourhood mediator.

Two members have a wholefood delivery business and two are the main carers for people coming for respite care. We have about seven acres of land on which we are growing vegetables organically in raised beds. We also have an orchard and we are caring for the woodland and marsh. We have goats, dogs, a cat, guinea pigs, gerbils, and fish in the pond. We welcome visitors to our Quaker meetings on Sundays, followed by vegetarian lunch on the first Sunday of the month. We have a working weekends on the first and third weekend of each month - enquiries by post only please and include a stamped addressed envelope. Sorry, but we do not have energy for visitors at other times.

QUAKER COMMUNITY AT BAMFORD

61

THE GUIDE TO COMMUNAL LIVING
DIGGERS & DREAMERS
94/95

Status
existing community

Address
Water Lane
Bamford
Derbyshire
S30 2DA

Telephone

Number of over 18s
15

Number of under 18s
5

Year started
1988

Situation
rural

Ideological focus
Quaker

Open to new members
Yes

QUAKER COMMUNITY PROJECT

Further to the work started by Diana and Frank Keegan, we have established a small group sharing a vision of living as a community with a Quaker focus, designed to provide a close and caring home for people of all ages from birth to death. While living as simply as possible we hope to create a way of life that is challenging and constructive. A place of integrity and creativity. We hope to find a site that, while rural, is part of a village or small town and enquiries are welcome from those who are keen to share in worship together as a basis for exploring ecologically sound ways of living and building socially useful projects.

We envisage a group of about six to eight households to include singles, couples and families having some shared meals and communal areas, but also their own private spaces. We recognise the needs of us all for freedom to grow and develop and we aim to remain flexible in supporting individual aspirations while balancing them with the collective needs of the group. We have faith that a purpose will emerge with our community's development which will make some contribution towards the healing of our world and demonstrate an alternative way of living.

Status
embryonic community

Address
care of
68 Lylton Road
Cowley
OXFORD
OX4 3NZ

Telephone
0865 718240

Number of over 18s

Number of under 18s

Year started

Situation

Ideological focus
Quaker

Open to new members

Radical Routes has grown out of a number of groups of mainly young unemployed people who during the late eighties set up co-operatives to house themselves and start up radical projects. The network has been able to help a number of co-operative communities to set up and provide many forms of support for its members. We have set up a national secondary co-operative (a co-op of co-ops) to create a formal structure of mutual aid between members - each member co-op agrees to work on radical/ecological projects and work together for mutual benefit. Each co-op agrees to take on some of the work/promotion so that it is fairly shared out and we avoid the development of a careerist central bureaucracy - passive membership situation. New co-ops are helped on the basis that they will fulfil these conditions and work to help other co-ops in return for the help they receive.

The secondary co-op also acts as an ethical investment agency for members, combining all the members' credibility to raise investments from the general public. The money is then loaned to member co-ops to expand; or to finance new co-ops. This is the only national investment scheme which is run and controlled by co-ops for the benefit of co-ops. Several new ventures have now started up with Radical Routes loans and with our first national launch under way, we are looking to be able to fund many more projects in the future.

Radical Routes is open to new member co-ops and has quarterly gatherings/meetings which interested groups can attend. You need to attend three gatherings and agree to the various entry conditions in order to join. We also hold promotional events and training workshops such as our twice yearly "Taking Control" weekends on how to set up co-ops/communities/projects etc, with workshops run by people involved in such ventures.

63

THE GUIDE TO COMMUNAL **LIVING**

DIGGERS & DREAMERS

94/95

Status
network

Address
25a Stanley Road
Whalley Range
MANCHESTER
M16 8HS

Telephone
061 232 9094

Number of over 18s

Number of under 18s

Year started
1986

Situation
urban and rural

Ideological focus
radical/ecological

Open to new members

RAINBOW HOUSING CO-OP

THE GUIDE TO
COMMUNAL
LIVING
DIGGERS
-&-
DREAMERS
94/95

64

R ainbow is a fully mutual housing co-operative owning its own housing stock, having bought the twenty-four houses in Spencer Street from the *Milton Keynes Development Corporation* in 1992. It has been in existence for 15 years and has always been responsible for the management and maintenance of the houses and the landscaping. The houses were originally constructed in Victorian times and were renovated in 1977. The street between the two rows of terraced cottages has been pedestrianised and landscaped. This provides a pleasant and convivial place to live.

Being quite small it is possible for all the members to know each other. There is mutual support and members often share meals together and help each other with tasks such as child care. Rainbow members themselves do most of the management, maintenance and landscaping. Working together promotes friendship as well as getting the jobs done. The money saved by doing things themselves has enabled the provision of facilities for the members. Rainbow makes decisions at General Meetings which are open to all members. It tries to make decisions by consensus but where this cannot be achieved a majority vote is used.

Status
existing community

Address
9 Spencer Street
New Bradwell
MILTON KEYNES
MK13 0DW

Telephone
0908 314685

Number of over 18s
27

Number of under 18s
19

Year started
1978

Situation
urban

Ideological focus
mixed

Open to new members
Yes

Redfield was in the wave of communities set up in big country houses in the late 1970s. It was never meant to be a "get-away-from-it-all commune" and although a fair amount of food is grown on the 17 acre estate we're not self-sufficient. We have sheep, chickens, great crested newts, ducks and a goat. Considerable energy has been expended on clearance and replanting of woodland to ensure future fuel supplies. Permacultural design techniques are in use in certain areas. Communal work (building maintenance; estate; and various household jobs) gets done most of the time but there are periods when little happens. Many systems have been tried over the years and, to be honest, we're still experimenting! Sustainability means something different to all of us and consequently it's often difficult to identify true collective aims and appropriate organisational structures. None of this worries the kids (several of whom are home-educated) - they have a whale of a time here. There's also a fine crop of very accomplished young people in their late teens and early 20s, who were brought up here and are now out there in the world.

Legally we're a housing co-op so we're all tenants and responsible for our own rent. In the past, this has usually meant outside work but more recently we've looked at creating employment on site. Living *and* working together is a whole new area that we've never really had to deal with before and we're still learning! We've brought to life some of the ideas that inspired the community at its inception - ideas which revolved around bringing more people from the outside to Redfield to do and learn things here. We've set up the *Redfield Foundation* as an educational charity which runs courses and events in the areas of: environment; food production; crafts and arts; community service; and equal opportunities. The *Redfield Centre* is a 16-bed residential facility which provides accommodation for our own courses and also those of outside facilitators. The *Nicht Gallery* runs an exhibition programme in which it displays the work of artists, both from within and without the Community. We're much better connected than we were and the locals no longer think that we're Moonies!

We want the Community to be active in the wider world as well as a home to its members so we're looking for people who have a positive reason to be here other than just "giving communal living a try".

REDFIELD
COMMUNITY

65

THE GUIDE TO
COMMUNAL
LIVING
DIGGERS &
DREAMERS

94/95

Status
existing community

Address
Buckingham Road
WINSLOW
Buckinghamshire
MK18 3LZ

Telephone
0296 713661

Electronic mail
redfield@gn.apc.org

Number of over 18s
15

Number of under 18s
10

Year started
1978

Situation
rural

Ideological focus
sustainability

Open to new members
Yes

RITHERDON ROAD COMMUNITY

THE GUIDE TO COMMUNAL LIVING
DIGGERS & DREAMERS
94/95

66

W e are a group of seven gay men living together communally in a wonderful house near Tooting Bec Common in south London. Our inspiration came from Wild Lavender - mentioned elsewhere in *Diggers and Dreamers* - with whom we are closely allied. Our intention is to provide mutual support for ourselves in a caring environment and to reach out to the brotherhood of gay men around us.

All of us are committed in one way or another to personal growth, to a holistic approach to health and to working towards a non-oppressive society. Amongst us we have experience in psychotherapy, dream therapy, group work, co-operatives, games, counselling, co-counselling, training and exploring our creativity through music and art. One of the group's principal aims is to provide support for people with AIDS or HIV.

Our most significant commitment to the communal ideal is participation in regular weekly house meetings. In these we sort out the humdrum details of running a household, preserve group and individual sanity by attending to the variety of interpersonal 'stuff' that inevitably arises between us and, when necessary, we take personal time to deal with our own individual concerns and emotions. Outside the house we cover, between us, a surprisingly wide range of work patterns - voluntary work, full-time study, full-time employment, freelance psychotherapy, freelance group therapy, part-time employment and part-time study. In addition to all this, members of the group organise 'Gay Men's Weeks' (GMWs) and other *Edward Carpenter Community* events such as games weekends and GMW reunion parties.

Status
existing community

Address
37 Ritherdon Road
Tooting Bec
LONDON
SW17 8QE

Telephone
081 672 8857

Number of over 18s
7

Number of under 18s

Year started
1987

Situation
urban

Ideological focus
gay men

Open to new members
Yes

Rivendell seeks, as its name implies, to be a "safe place in the wilderness", and occupies a Victorian farmhouse in the very lovely Lune Valley on the border of Westmorland and the Yorkshire Dales. Our main work is caring for people who come for short breaks from all sorts of stressful situations. The "therapy" offered is interaction with country things: care of goats, hens and pony, walking, riding, sailing, gardening, music, reading and (not least) people with time to talk and listen. We are, usually, a core family of three plus three volunteers who come for varying periods. Each of us has a personal room which leaves four guest rooms. The "work" is caring for the practical and emotional needs of guests, cleaning and maintenance of house and garden, animal care, and admin. The basis is Christian but not denominational and open to the wisdom of other faiths and philosophies; we begin and end the day with short periods of worship and thoughtfulness. Rivendell is associated with the Iona Community as a "Columban House". There is an element of leadership from the core family but we do try to make decisions by consensus and all work is shared on rota systems. Members are largely vegetarian but we do eat fish and dairy products. Gardening and animal husbandry is organic; we have a fair sized garden and small paddock. The house is leasehold, the "community" is an unincorporated association which includes the residents and other local supporters. There is an associated charitable trust which helps in subsidising guests who cannot donate their costs. New volunteers can occasionally be accepted. Please do not telephone after 7.30pm.

RIVENDELL COMMUNITY

67

THE GUIDE TO COMMUNAL **LIVING**
DIGGERS *&* DREAMERS
94/95

Status
existing community

Address
Rigmarden Farmhouse Mansergh CARNFORTH Lancashire LA6 2ET

Telephone
05242 76265

Number of over 18s
6

Number of under 18s

Year started
1986

Situation
rural

Ideological focus
Christian

Open to new members
Yes

SALISBURY CENTRE

THE GUIDE TO
COMMUNAL
LIVING
DIGGERS &
DREAMERS
94/95

68

Status
existing community

Address
2 Salisbury Road
EDINBURGH
EH16 5AB

Telephone
031 667 5438

Number of over 18s
7

Number of under 18s
1

Year started
1973

Situation
urban

Ideological focus
ecological

Open to new members
Yes

The Salisbury Centre was established in 1973 by an active Sufi meditation group and Dr Winifred Rushforth, a leading Scottish psychotherapist and dreamworker. They had a shared vision for the centre. They saw it as a place that would offer people somewhere to openly explore different paths of spiritual renewal as well as somewhere that psychological and physical healing work could be done. This is still the Community's focus.

The Centre is a large Georgian house with a self-contained flat upstairs with separate rooms for seven residents, where we live together communally. We grow our own veggies in the large organic garden out the back. The other half of the house has a meditation room, pottery, studio, kitchen, library, office and spare room for small groups or passing visitors. Caring for this space, running courses in all things 'alternative', arranging rentals and general administration provides part-time work and a basic income for five of us - working as a co-operative with consensus decision making and a lot of trust and humour. The property is still owned by a Trust and is an educational charity. The workers and the Trustees have an open and creative relationship. Life at the Centre can be crazy chaos: doorbells ringing, endless enquiries, the cats being sick. Then there are long holidays, mostly quiet (except during theEdinburgh Festival), a chance to restore ourselves and maintain the building and garden. Overall there is some binding purpose: that we continue to explore new ways of living and working for all our futures.

S arana Community was formed in 1989 when a number of friends who had met through the *Bristol Buddhist Centre* decided to live together. One of the original community members purchased the house and, although having since left the community, he has kept up the property for the express purpose of housing a men's Buddhist community. All members have expressed a commitment to Buddhist principles, particularly as taught by Sangharakshita, the founder of the *Friends of the Western Buddhist Order*. Hence, our living together is an attempt to practise the principles of Sangha or spiritual community - one of the three Jewels or Refuges of Buddhism. "Sarana" itself means "Refuge" in the sense of being the heart's only true source of happiness in a changing world. We are a men's community, as we feel that the bonds of friendship we are trying to establish with one another are best nurtured in a situation free from sexual polarity and tension. No financial commitment is required of members (other than rent) and means of livelihood is left up to individuals. All of us do, however, have some involvement in the *Buddhist Centre*. We eat together every evening, have a community evening once a week and sometimes meditate together in the mornings in the communal shrine room. Some members share rooms whilst others have their own. The community evening is the main focus of the week and is a lively mix of study (on Buddhist themes), discussion, reporting-in or Buddhist devotional meditation practice.

SARANA COMMUNITY

69

THE GUIDE TO
COMMUNAL
LIVING
DIGGERS &
DREAMERS
94/95

Status
existing community

Address
care of Diggers and Dreamers

Telephone
✆!

Number of over 18s
7

Number of under 18s

Year started
1989

Situation
urban

Ideological focus
Buddhist

Open to new members
Yes

SCARGILL HOUSE

THE GUIDE TO COMMUNAL **LIVING**

DIGGERS & DREAMERS

94/95

70

Status
existing community

Address
Kettlewell
SKIPTON
North Yorkshire
BD23 5HU

Telephone
0756 760234/760315

Number of over 18s
39+

Number of under 18s
2

Year started
1959

Situation
rural

Ideological focus
Christian

Open to new members
Yes

Scargill House is a holiday and conference centre in the Yorkshire Dales which opened in 1959 as a centre of evangelism and renewal for the churches in the North of England. Although it is an Anglican foundation the original vision included staffing the centre with a Community of Christians from all walks of life and Christian denominations. The establishment now includes 39 working members of Community with wives and families in addition. Community members are divided into six teams - Chaplaincy, House, Kitchen, Pantry, Estate and Office covering the various functions of running what is basically a conference centre but with the addition of Christian input. All Community members have an opportunity of leading worship and of ministering to the guests. The programme is divided into two seasons, the Conference season which includes parish weekends, retreats, school visits, specialist programmes on eg prayer or healing and some secular bookings. The Summer Holiday Houseparty season includes week long holidays for guests from the UK and abroad.

The prime purpose of the Community is to serve the guests. Community members eat in the dining room with the guests. The majority of Community members are single, lay and young but the Chaplaincy team comprises priests, women deacons and lay readers. The overall policy of Scargill House is the responsibility of the Council who are prominent members of the Church, both lay and ordained. The buildings can accommodate 90 guests and apart from several large lounges for conferences there is a fine Chapel, Library, Quiet Room and Games Room. Enquiries for private bookings should be made to the Bookings Secretary, for conference to the Conference Secretary and for Community membership to the Administrator.

The Sheiling is part of the wider Camphill Movement, based on the philosophy of Rudolph Steiner and the therapeutic work of Karl König. The aim of the Sheiling is to create a supportive environment in which each individual, handicapped or not, can contribute in a meaningful way to the well-being of the whole, and find recognition, understanding and healing. The Sheiling has developed into a diverse community comprising a school, college and training for adults. It is situated on over 50 acres of land about a mile from Ringwood. There is also a farm five miles away. The total community, of over 250 people, has 17 family houses of various sizes, located next to gardens, fields and woodlands. Each residence is a self-contained house shared by children, adolescents, or adults with a mental handicap, together with co-workers of all ages and, very often, their own children, creating a fully integrated 'extended family'.

The community has a rich and varied cultural life. The celebration of the Christian Festivals enhances the experience of the seasons of the year, and Sunday mornings are marked by interdenominational services. Many other cultural activities are supported too. Children attend school classes according to their age and irrespective of mental abilities. The curriculum is based on the Rudolph Steiner philosophy. Students in the college learn social and manual skills and are encouraged to achieve their full human potential. The farms and workshops enable community members to participate in bakery, weaving, pottery, agriculture and horticulture.

Life at the Sheiling is always demanding and often involves a good deal of responsibility. Living and working together - sharing life with people of all ages and with a wide range of capabilities as well as limitations - is a constant challenge. House-parents, teachers, therapists, craft tutors, farmers, gardeners are all co-workers in the mutually supportive tasks of helping each other create a striving, therapeutic environment. Co-workers who live in the Sheiling do so as full-time volunteers. They receive no salary but work in answer to the needs of others, while in return their own needs are provided for, including some pocket money. Through this viable alternative to the wage system, it becomes possible to develop a sense of mutual involvement and responsibility. Qualifications and previous experience are not necessary, but it is necessary to have a warm, compassionate and realistic interest in those who need our special care.

SHEILING CAMPHILL COMMUNITY

71

THE GUIDE TO COMMUNAL **LIVING**
DIGGERS *&* DREAMERS
94/95

Status
existing community

Address
Sheiling School
Horton Road
Ashley
RINGWOOD
Hampshire
BH24 2EB

Telephone
0425 477488

Number of over 18s
160

Number of under 18s
90

Year started
1942

Situation
rural

Ideological focus
Anthroposophy

Open to new members
Yes

SHRUBB FAMILY

THE GUIDE TO
COMMUNAL
LIVING
DIGGERS
&
DREAMERS
94/95

72

Status
existing community

Address
*Shrubb Farm Cottages
Larling
East Harling
NORWICH
NR16 2QT*

Telephone

Number of over 18s
6

Number of under 18s
4

Year started
1970

Situation
rural

Ideological focus
*ecological/environ-
mental*

Open to new members

Home to a community since 1968, Shrubb is an anachronism in post-Thatcherite Britain. The 17th century cottage is a working example of stewardship. Owned by Shrubb Family Ltd, all community members are directors of the company - new members pay no capital on joining and take no money on leaving. In spite of this hopelessly idealistic management system, the buildings and community have prospered and even survived a major fire in the early 1980s. A timber framed/clay lump building dating back to the Seventeenth century, it was originally three farm workers cottages.

We are not income sharing. We sign on when necessary. We all contribute to the upkeep of house and stomachs. There is no joining capital. Cooking, domestic chores, relaxation and toilet facilities are all shared and decisions are made by consensus. We are mostly vegetarian and although not self-sufficient, we grow a fair amount of our vegetables. Everyone has their own bedroom - all other rooms are communal.

By pure chance three newcomers to the community are permaculture design course graduates and the process of "perming" Shrubb began in spring 1992. Our one acre plot certainly presents a challenge. It's surrounded by typical East Anglian wheatlands, with few trees and very little hedgerow. The badly degraded breckland soil, sandy and shallow, overlies boulder clay which in turn covers chalk bedrock. It turns to dust in summer and compacts with amazing ease in winter. As a bonus all the cultivated areas were badly infested with perennial weeds!

We welcome visitors who enjoy working and want to gain practical experience and help develop temperate permacultural techniques. We have many skills to share - not least good food, laughter and music. If you would like to visit Shrubb Family please contact us well in advance.

The Simon Community was founded in 1963 by Anton Wallich-Clifford. We are a community of volunteers and homeless people living together in two houses and a night shelter in London and a small farm in Kent. Our work consists partly of our mission of caring for homeless people, in the form of running a shelter giving people a few nights break from the streets, doing tea-runs and clothes-runs and organising a lot of outreach work to meet people on the streets. The other branch of our work is in campaigning for and with homeless people on various issues, topical or ongoing. Amongst other things, we publish a quarterly newsletter, the *Simon Star*, with news about the Community and developments in the field of homelessness. We have a policy of not accepting government funding and raise all our financial requirement ourselves through donations and collections.

Simon is an active community and all those living in it are asked to give of themselves in whatever way they can. We meet very regularly in our houses and on a Community-wide basis to share ideas and discussions, make decisions and review our Community. Simon is very much about sharing in an often chaotic and tiring environments, which requires a regular structure. Many people, homeless and volunteers, come through Simon in a year: as on the streets, stability is an elusive element. Our philosophy is one of acceptance of people on their terms and at their level. We attempt to live as a "bridge" between the "normal" world and that of the rough sleeper. In a sense everyone in Simon is a "misfit", and as a Community we are one too. We are not stable, or overtly therapeutic, or organisationally efficient. Simon has its very own spirit and its very own history.

We welcome enquiries and are willing to send information to anyone who requests it. If you wish to be added to our mailing list for the *Simon Star*, please let us know. We also have a fairly regular demand for volunteers to live and work with us. Ideally we would like people to come for at least six months. Our minimum age requirement is 19 years old. Please write for details.

SIMON COMMUNITY

73

THE GUIDE TO COMMUNAL **LIVING**
DIGGERS *&* DREAMERS
94/95

Status
existing community

Address
PO Box 1187
LONDON
NW5 4HW

Telephone
071 485 6639

Number of over 18s
45

Number of under 18s
0

Year started
1963

Situation
urban & rural

Ideological focus
none

Open to new members
Yes

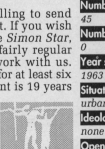

SOLARIS
(PROVISIONAL NAME)

THE GUIDE TO
COMMUNAL
LIVING

DIGGERS
-&-
DREAMERS

94/95

74

Status
embryonic community

Address
care of
46 Butlers Grove
Great Linford
MILTON KEYNES
MK14 5DT

Telephone
0908 231217

Number of over 18s
70

Number of under 18s

Year started

Situation
urban

Ideological focus
green, ecological
(socialist)

Open to new members
Yes

The community is proposed to be a newbuild scheme in Milton Keynes along the lines of a Co-housing scheme (see *Cohousing* by McCamant & Durrett (1988)). The core group consistes of people experienced in co-operative living. We aim to have about 30 houses and, very importantly, a good sized community house. The scheme may be a mixture of self-build houses and houses built by a contractor. Self-build houses allow for an input of labour rather than capital, which will help less well-off people - it also allows for a flexibility and personalising of the house design. In any case, we hope that design of the scheme will involve close interaction between the architects and the future inhabitants.

Milton Keynes has been selected as a site since it is where the group is currently based, and also because there seems to be a good possibility of getting some land with building permission. We have already had preliminary contacts with the *Commission for the New Towns*; the *Milton Keynes Borough Council*; and *Ecological Development*. We are currently investigating various possibilities for financing the scheme ranging from mainly public finance (from the *Housing Corporation*) to full private ownership, with a range of shared-ownership possibilities in between.

We all have a 'green' focus and the scheme is intended to incorporate state of the art ecological design such as excellent insulation and maximum use of solar energy. We intend the community to strike the right balance between useful communal facilities and scope for privacy and independence. We plan for the possibility of a communal restaurant in the community house, and good space for shared workshops, venue space etc. We would also like to have some shared garden and gardening space. We anticipate that the shortest time to completion of the scheme will be about two years (circa 1995). We are interested in hearing from anyone who would like to participate in this exciting project.

SOME FRIENDS COMMUNITY

Some Friends is a community in the East End of London, which grew out of a London Quaker Action group in the early 1970s. Many of us have conventional jobs to go to, others are unwaged. Decisions are taken by consensus at regular meetings. We pay the same monthly rent, and there is a sliding scale for food costs. We do not share incomes.

We share a number of ideals, including non-violence, vegetarianism, equality of the sexes, and simple living. Our individual beliefs vary. Some of us are Quakers. Others are influenced by a range of spiritual traditions, or have no desire for membership or label. We have relationships meetings separate from business meetings and are commited to trying to resolve inter-personal conflicts in a spirit of honesty and non-violence. We live in two groups, roughly equal in size, on three floors over a shop. Both 'households' have a kitchen, where we share communal meals most evenings. Each member has their own room, with a shared living room. We are open to enquirers. Please write.

75

THE GUIDE TO COMMUNAL LIVING

DIGGERS & DREAMERS

94/95

Status
existing community

Address
*128 Bethnal Green
Road
London
E2 6DG*

Telephone

Number of over 18s
14

Number of under 18s
2

Year started
1973

Situation
urban

Ideological focus
non violence

Open to new members

SOME PEOPLE IN LEICESTER

76

Some People in Leicester (SPIL) is a city based co-operative network with a variety of aspects, of which co-operative housing is one option. There are two levels to SPIL. One is the loose community where many people and ideas may interact in a low key network of practical co-operation. Providing continuity to this network there is a smaller group of people (two at present but ideally three to five) intending a lifelong commitment to each other, based on sharing of emotional and financial resources: we call this the core group. Members share common values of accountability, loyalty and responsibility. We believe that power and responsibility should be closely linked and accept the elitist impications of the principle of workers' power applied to social life.

Our practical activities include: co-operative work (we have a well-established electrical and building business); vehicle sharing; shared child-care; income pooling; co-operative housing; capital pooling; organic gardening. We hope to expand and develop all our projects, but in particular want to build up our small radical bookshop, and also to cultivate more allotments.

As we try to remain as independent as possible from the System, our economic base is an important focus for our energies. We feel it is vital that local groups do not exist in isolation but are involved in wider struggles and broader visions - our aim is to change the world. We are full members of *Radical Routes* Secondary Co-op - a network of radical housing and worker co-ops, with members in various cities and towns, and even a few in the country! Some of us are also working for people power - direct democracy, regional autonomy, recovering our lost history and culture.

Activities range from street and neighbourhood groups to the Movement for Middle England and Da Engliscan Gesithas (English Companions). The numbers indicated alongside indicate people participating in at least one of our structures of co-operation. Our urban focus should be understood in the context of a diverse network of socialist, co-operative, anarchist and green activity in Leicester, of which our 'lifestyle politics' is only a tiny part. We welcome worker-visitors by arrangement.

Status
existing community

Address
12 Bartholomew Street
LEICESTER
LE2 1FA

Telephone
0533 545436/541403

Number of over 18s
15

Number of under 18s
7

Year started
1978

Situation
urban

Ideological focus
co-operative

Open to new members
Yes

We are a spiritually-based community group. Our aims are to establish and maintain spiritual family; and to develop love-based (as opposed to fear-based) structures around relationships, children, work, sex, money, education, health, aging, birth and death. For us, being spiritually-based means learning to trust ourselves and our own intuition, and to apply personal spiritual beliefs (whatever they are) to every aspect of our lives. We've found that we need to be very open about our relationships both inside and outside the group, so no relationships are taken for granted, and no emotional areas are "off-limits": we all have the freedom to question any aspects of any relationship at any time. We have no leaders - members take full responsibility for themselves individually, and for the group as a whole, and all decisions are made through consensus. Most of us live together, and practise asset and income sharing, but it is always up to individuals to decide to what extent they want to do this. All work, inside or outside the community, paid or unpaid, is done on a purely voluntary basis. We prefer to grow through freedom rather than through obligation. Anyone who wants to join us is free to do so. At the time of writing (June 1993) we're without a permanent base; we are planning to be in the Bristol area for the next three years at least (the address is a contact address). There are very few areas of life which don't interest us, and projects with which we are already involved, and which we wish to set up, include:

- offering courses and workshops on a range of subjects: eg co-operative design, spiritual architecture, new science, alternative therapies, personal and social peacemaking, etc. These to be run on a non-commercial basis.
- sharing our facilities with the wider community, including space, tools, resources and ideas.
- having an open door policy: this would entail offering shelter and emotional and/or material support to anyone who might need it, as space and circumstances allow.
- participating in a network for any spiritually-based groups and communities which have been set up to experiment and work with new energy and ideas.
- offering enlightened support and facilities in the areas of birth, education, and the care of the terminally ill.
- active involvement in a Local Exchange Trading Scheme (LETS)
- electronic networking - you can contact us via electronic mail.

SPIRITUAL
FAMILY
COMMUNITY
GROUP

77

THE GUIDE TO
COMMUNAL
LIVING
DIGGERS & DREAMERS
94/95

Status
existing community

Address
*care of 6 Arbutus Dr
Coombe Dingle
BRISTOL
BS9 2PJ*

Telephone
0272 681941 ✆!

Electronic mail
community@gn.apc.org

Number of over 18s
4

Number of under 18s
1

Year started
1991

Situation
probably urban

Ideological focus
Spiritual

Open to new members
Yes

STROUD SUSTAINABLE VILLAGE PROJECT

The Stroud Sustainable Village Project is planning a village based on permaculture principles to be constructed in the Stroud district. The underlying principle is one of sustainability in energy, materials, natural resources and social structures. All buildings are to be constructed of ecologically sound materials (in collection, manufacture and use) and will be designed for low energy input. It is intended to have communal laundry and freezer facilities and that the village be self-sustaining in energy and collection and processing of water and sewage etc.

Some of the land will be communally held by the village trust for communal buildings, horticulture, workshops, wilderness areas and rented housing. Houses and gardens will be held freehold subject to certain covenants against using herbicides etc. Within the ethics of permaculture there will not be constraints on personal political or religious beliefs. Employment within the village in crafts and agriculture will be encouraged to counter the trend of commuting from a dormitary village, there will also be the possibilituy of a LETS system. Car use within the village will be discouraged by design however, the Sustainable Village Project is encouraging the use of new technology in design and construction provided that it is sustainable.

Interested parties can apply for an information brochure (£4.50) or become members (£15/annum or £250/life). The Project is affiliated to the *Permaculture Association of Britain.*

Status
embryonic community

Address
PO Box 3
STROUD
Gloucestershire
GL15 1YB

Telephone
0453 751500

Number of over 18s

Number of under 18s

Year started

Situation

Ideological focus

Open to new members
Yes

We are a very small housing co-op in Newcastle upon Tyne. Originally one house with seven single people, we have since expanded and now have another house in the same street, also housing seven single people. We have no ideological basis except the belief that decent housing is a right and that there should be alternatives to bedsitters, landlords and living with one other person. Everybody moving into the co-op is asked to make a commitment to co-operative living and contribute what skills and time they have. The co-op offers some control over one's living space and a chance to have a real say in how ones environment is organised. Obviously this takes place within the context of the Housing Bill and pressure from the *Housing Corporation* etc. Each house organises itself in domestic matters eg one house is vegetarian with no pets, the other omnivorous with cats! Both houses are mixed sexes with ages ranging between early twenties and late thirties. We have no children. We have a waiting list for applicants - please write, don't phone - for when vacancies occur. Applicants are chosen on the basis of housing need, commitment to the co-op and compatibility with the people already in the house they apply to. We are very "ordinary people" with a variety of "ordinary" jobs. The shared house we live in is our home, with many advantages such as warmth, good food, washing machines, rented video etc that would be difficult or impossible if we were all living singly. We have companionship and support but also privacy in our own bedrooms when we want it. Our official decision making body is the monthly co-op meeting, and each house also has monthly meetings for 'house affairs'. Relationships within the houses obviously change as people come and go, but we do not have a policy on these and indeed the individuals within each house influence how communal we are at any given time. In certain areas, ie meetings, rents policy, allocations, we are very structured, but this has proved to be a strength in the ten years we have existed as it gives each house a great deal of freedom in other areas.

SUMMERHILL HOUSING CO-OP

79

THE GUIDE TO COMMUNAL **LIVING**
DIGGERS & DREAMERS
94/95

Status
existing community

Address
6 Summerhill Terrace
NEWCASTLE UPON TYNE
NE4 6EB

Telephone

Number of over 18s
14

Number of under 18s
0

Year started
1980

Situation
urban

Ideological focus
co-operation

Open to new members
Yes

THAT COMMUNITY

THE GUIDE TO COMMUNAL LIVING

DIGGERS & DREAMERS

94/95

80

THAT Community in Birmingham is managed by Trident Housing Association and is run as a residential home. It is a therapeutic community for emotionally and psychologically disturbed adults (upper age limit 35 years approximately., It offers a secure base for residents to make long-term committed attachments. A skilled supportive staff group are available round-the-clock. The therapeutic focus is on unmet developmental needs. Members of the community are expected to maintain a level of socially acceptable behaviour and contract with each other to respond appropriately to caring confrontation to facilitate this. The residents form a supportive peer group and together do all the shopping, cooking and cleaning within the community. In time each resident may need the support of others whilst working through difficult problems. Often another peer will have resolved a similar problem and they can understand and help using their own experience. This involvement is invaluable in keeping to a minimum potential disruptions and peer pressure leads to appropriate behaviour.

Personal and group psychotherapy with professional therapists takes place daily and residents have individual therapy contracts, which are revised on an ongoing basis. A safe, structured reactive environment offers a full programme of training and support in social and life skills. Residents use the structure and support in place of medication which, when necessary, they reduce and stop gradually under medical supervision. The long term goal is for residents to be capable of operating independently and productively in normal society without further need for professional support. Ex-residents remain community members and stay in touch after they leave. Admission is by referral from health and social care professionals. Fees are negotaible and based on a jointly agreed assessment of need. Visitors with a professional interest are welcome by prior arrangement.

Status
existing community

Address
care of Diggers and Dreamers

Telephone

Number of over 18s
30

Number of under 18s
10

Year started
1988

Situation
urban

Ideological focus
caring

Open to new members
Yes

S ix family houses on a 135 acre dairy farm, living as a small intentional village with connections with Prinknash Benedictine Abbey next door. We began during the war as a pacifist commune in Cornwall and moved here in 1952 after a long inner search through Jungian psychology and the East to the Catholic Church. In 1961 we changed to a village and since then each family has been financially separate and developed varying interests and occupations.

Our central act as a community is the weekly celebration of Mass in our chapel by one of the monks from the Abbey, though there are many living here who are not members of any church. Occupations at the present include farming, silversmithing, stone and woodcarving, pottery, counselling, T'ai Chi Ch'uan, painting and calligraphy, teaching. Visitors are welcome but please contact us first and bring sheets or sleeping bag and towel. We ask for £5 per day or what you can afford.

TAENA

81

THE GUIDE TO
COMMUNAL
LIVING
DIGGERS &
DREAMERS
94/95

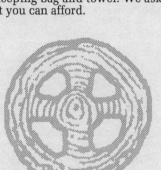

Status
existing community

Address
care of Diggers and Dreamers

Telephone

Number of over 18s
15

Number of under 18s
7

Year started
1941

Situation
rural

Ideological focus
Christian

Open to new members
No

TALAMH

THE GUIDE TO
COMMUNAL
LIVING
DIGGERS
-&-
DREAMERS
94/95

82

Status
existing community

Address
Birkhill House
COALBURN
Lanarkshire
ML11 0NJ

Telephone
055582 555

Number of over 18s
5

Number of under 18s
0

Year started
1993

Situation
rural

Ideological focus
ecological

Open to new members
Yes

Talamh (earth/soil) is a group of five (probably six by the time that this book is published - Heather and Ian are expecting). We started in January 1993 and have a 16th Century farmhouse and 50 acres of land to be managed as species habitat with a fun/education space. Our focus is the environment and people. We are aiming for self-sufficiency.

We would like to be a venue for education in energy efficiency and renewable methods of production, environmental education and holistic health and individual development by having an atmosphere where people can relax, take time for themselves and learn from or give to Talamh. We have monthly working (learning) weekends and occasional weeks. In the near future our first educational programme may involve gardening to dyking; shiatsu to counselling; stargazing to circus skills.

We income share and have weekly meetings. Decisions are made by consensus, but with each of us having an area of responsibility on which we report to the meeting. Just now three out of the five have full time jobs, two of which are outside Talamh. We aim for that to be two out of five working from home - one with *Greenpeace*, the other *Talamh Technology* (exploring and developing electronics/computers for sustainable lifestyles, ie renewable energy). We cook mostly vegetarian food and will cater for meat eaters and vegans. We can offer accommodation for sleeping visitors and any number of day visitors are welcome. Talamh awaits ...

Taraloka Buddhist Women's Community exists to run a Buddhist retreat centre for women, but it is also a spiritual community wherein the residents actively pursue the Buddhist way of life together. The community has a daily programme of meditation, work, communal meals, and also weekly business meetings, study groups, etc. We are constituted as a charity. There is no entry fee, although new prospective members pay their own way for the three months of their trial period. If they are accepted as members they receive basic support. Decisions are arrived at through consensus. Each member plays a rôle in running the retreat centre.

Celibacy is observed by all members on the premises, although members are free to pursue sexual relationships elsewhere should they so wish. We actively pursue friendships with one another, trying to encourage one another to develop spiritually. We follow basic Buddhist ethical precepts, the most important of which is the practice of non-violence, or loving-kindness. As part of this ethos we are all vegetarians. We are housed in a large farmhouse and are gradually converting the farm outbuildings to house the Retreat Centre. The conversion work has been done largely by teams of women volunteers. Further information on our courses and retreats isavailable from the secretary.

TARALOKA BUDDHIST RETREAT CENTRE FOR WOMEN

83

THE GUIDE TO
COMMUNAL
LIVING
DIGGERS &
DREAMERS
94/95

Status
existing community

Address
Cornhill Farm
Bettisfield
WHITCHURCH
Shropshire
SY13 2LD

Telephone
094 875 646

Number of over 18s
8

Number of under 18s
0

Year started
1985

Situation
rural

Ideological focus
Buddhist

Open to new members
No

TIPI VILLAGE

THE GUIDE TO
COMMUNAL
LIVING

DIGGERS &
DREAMERS

94/95

84

Status
existing community

Address
Marchoglwyn Fawr
Llanfynydd
CARMARTHEN
Dyfed
SA32 7UQ

Telephone
0558 685556

Number of over 18s
80

Number of under 18s
40

Year started
1976

Situation
rural

Ideological focus
eco-pagan

Open to new members
Yes

The Tipi Village community is dedicated to living lightly upon the Earth and in harmony with the natural environment. We live in native North American style tipis in over 100 acres of Welsh hill land. Each tipi is an individual or family "household", so our community is very much a tribal village rather than a commune, but a village with a high component of communal activity and inter-action. Our land is partly owned by individuals and partly owned in trust on behalf of the community as a whole. We share a large tipi (the "Big Lodge") which functions as a communal space for parties, celebrations, get-togethers and (very rare) meetings, as well as accommodation for visitors and guests. We also share regular sweat lodges (saunas) and a collectively run shop.

We regard all of our land as a nature reserve in which humans can live in integrated harmony with nature. Formal structure and organisation are minimal, verging on non-existent, but we have a collective land fund to which all contribute in order to add, periodically, to our trust land holding. We have no hierarchy or elected authority, but long-standing members are regarded as tribal elders with organically developed rôles and influence. Decisions (when absolutely necessary) are made by consensus and enforced by collective social pressure.

We have a co-operative extended tribal family attitude towards childcare. Most babies are born by natural home birth. Some children are home educated but an increasing number now attend local schools. We grow much of our own vegetables in individual and family organic gardens and (being dependent on firewood for fuel) we are particularly keen on tree planting. Visitors are welcome but dogs are definitely not and parking space for vehicles is strictly limited. Please send a stamped addressed envelope with all enquiries.

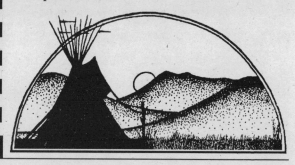

This is the situation here at present: We are four men and two children (half the time) living in a small inner city community

- we eat communally and have a vegan diet.
- although individual members are involved in various projects in the wider community there are no specific house projects that we all work on, other than the upkeep of the house
- we have a large front room which we sometimes let out to local groups and we have some office equipment which is sometimes used as a resource by people outside the house
- we organise a food co-op (bulk buying from wholesalers) with a group of people from outside the house
- whilst we welcome visitors we have no specific tasks for visitors to get involved in other than whatever house task we are doing at the time. Also we may not be able to spend much time with visitors while they are here. Having said that we are happy for people to phone up and to arrange a time when they can stay. Visitors are welcome to eat with us and to sleep here, but other that we cannot guarantee to offer much more than a place to stay when they are in Bristol.

We are open to new members if and when there is space.

TWO MULES HOUSING CO-OP

85

THE GUIDE TO COMMUNAL **LIVING**
DIGGERS *&* DREAMERS
94/95

Status	
existing community	
Address	
34 Bellevue Road	
Easton	
BRISTOL	
BS5 6DS	
Telephone	
0272 522131 ⎇!	
Number of over 18s	
4	
Number of under 18s	
2	
Year started	
Situation	
urban	
Ideological focus	
Open to new members	
Yes	

VEGAN COMMUNITY HOUSING COLLECTIVE

THE GUIDE TO COMMUNAL LIVING

DIGGERS & DREAMERS

94/95

86

Status
embryonic community

Address
care of
31 Caerau Road
Caerau, Maesteg
BRIDGEND
Mid Glamorgan
CF34 0PB

Telephone

Number of over 18s

Number of under 18s

Year started
1988

Situation
urban

Ideological focus
ecological

Open to new members
Yes

At the time of writing, there are only two of us here, Bob Howes since inception, October 1988, and Brian Scattergood since August 1991. We are waiting for grant work to be done on the house before being keen on new members joining. It should all be done by 1994. We are planning domestic heat recovery and a better wood-burner with forced air central heating/ventilation as well as radiators to make the place comfortable as well as reasonably eco-logical/economical.

We have plenty of solar panels and plan to charge batteries with them to save on mains electricity. We have two *286 PC* computers and plan to use one as an electronic mail bulletin board in order to distribute eco info to the business world, especially info on our design of compact eco-cities of the future. These compact cities will be communities of communities rather than communes. They will contain communes, families, multiple marriages and individuals in constant flux, ever changing and growing. Food production and consumption will be shared rather than money-based.

Towards this end we have three allotments where we grow some of our food. We augment this with skip food. We are vegan. All letters answered, please say lots about yourself. No smoking in the house.

The community was formed in 1979 with the purpose of converting a large 1862 classical mansion, Whitbourne Hall, into twenty flats. This process was completed in 1987. Besides the main house and ornamental buildings there is a walled kitchen garden, paddock, ornamental gardens and pineatum for use by community members. Presently about forty people aged six months to seventy-five live at the Hall.

The community is structured as a company limited by guarantee with one share being owned by each of the twenty flat owners. A Management Committee is elected at the Annual General Meeting with policy decided at general meetings. Flats are bought and sold on the open market. On purchase each owner becomes a leaseholder, a one twentieth sharer of the freehold and a member of the company. Each owner is required to pay a monthly maintenance charge (presently £50) to cover building insurance, sewerage, common lighting and general upkeep of the land and buildings.

WHITBOURNE HALL COMMUNITY

87

THE GUIDE TO COMMUNAL **LIVING**

DIGGERS &
DREAMERS

94/95

Status
existing community

Address
Whitbourne
WORCESTER
WR6 5SE

Telephone
0886 21147

Number of over 18s
20

Number of under 18s
25

Year started
1979

Situation
rural

Ideological focus

Open to new members
Yes

WILD LAVENDER

THE GUIDE TO
COMMUNAL
LIVING

DIGGERS -&-
DREAMERS

88

94/95

Status
existing community

Address
34 Queensdown Road
Hackney Downs
LONDON
E5 8NN

Telephone

Number of over 18s
6

Number of under 18s
0

Year started
1981

Situation
urban

Ideological focus
gay male

Open to new members
Yes

Wild Lavender began with a group of men who first met up in 1980 and began to discuss how gay men could live together in a mutually supportive environment. This is of major importance for gay men living in a society where we are faced with overt and oppressive heterosexism which can foster a sense of profound isolation. Thus we aim to build a secure and nurturing community which, for its members, complements the established gay male commercial 'scene'. Wild Lavender Housing Co-op was established in Leeds in 1981, with a number of men sharing a large house in Chapeltown. Since then there have been many changes in membership and emphasis. From a close-knit, intense, 'therapeutic process' group that planned to move into the countryside, it has developed into a more relaxed, avowedly urban household.

We are currently six men and a cat in a large Victorian house which we run communally. All chores and management tasks are shared, and members cook and eat together. Weekly meetings discuss co-op business, inter-personal relationships and life in general. We are committed to supporting each other and strive to achieve consensus when making decisions. Members' occupations vary from university lecturer to unemployed. Besides communal space, each person has one room to himself. We are non-smoking, eat vegetarian meals, and generally emphasise a holistic approach to life. Since its inception, Wild Lavender has been both a home and a resource for a large number of men, and members have been responsible for establishing other well known projects, such as Gay Men's Weeks at Laurieston Hall and the Edward Carpenter Community. Past residents have moved on to join rural communities, start other communal groups, fall in love, and even leave the country.

How to Visit a Community

If you're interested in communities then this book can help, but it's only the first step, the next obvious one being to visit a few. This could be an important step for you, but it's also important for most communities. We need visitors for fresh ideas, interest and energy, plus of course valuable help with the work. Visitors are also where new members come from, an important consideration for most communities.

Most if not all communities prefer you to arrange a visit and not just to turn up. The important thing to remember is that a community is home for its members, and it can feel less than comfortable to have your home filled with uninvited guests. Crabapple expects you to write, briefly explaining who you are and what you're looking for. It may be that we can straightaway tell for sure that this place won't suit you, but if that's not the case, we'll reply with a more detailed version of our directory entry in this book, updated if necessary. If you still want to come after reading our 'blurb' then a quick phone call can arrange a visit, usually of three or four days. The procedure isn't as complicated as it may sound.

So what can you expect when - having packed your sleeping-bag, wellies, working clothes and hot water bottle - you find yourself at the door of your chosen community? Well I'm afraid I can't tell you, not because it's a secret, but because not only do communities vary enormously, but you could come upon each one in a different state or mood.

Remember that however you find a community on your first visit, it isn't always like that. Generally however you can expect a nice cup of tea (or whatever you drink) and a tour around the place. You can expect to be asked to join in with whatever's going on, but you can always decline and ask if there's something more suited to your abilities and interests. One thing you can certainly expect is that help with the washing-up will be appreciated!

We do make an effort to help people feel at home but, partly because we have visitors nearly all the time, we sometimes don't put in as much effort as we'd like. I'm sure many communities are similar in this. I'd advise you to say if you feel neglected, either socially or for lack of things to do (it does happen!). If you feel shy or nervous, remember we were all visitors once and can probably remember what it was like.

What gets our backs up about visitors? Well, some do seem to forget that they're in someone's (many people's) home, and it's not pleasant to have your home treated like an institution. We're not, generally, frightened of being criticised or challenged, but there is a limit and it helps if first there is some attempt to understand not only how things are but also why. Personally I'm usually happy to answer any number of reasonable questions, but sometimes I feel - and it is irritating - that there is less interest in the answers than in the questions. As Kat Kinkade (from Twin Oaks

Community in the USA) has said: "Any community's favourite visitor is the cheerful, helpful one who is genuinely impressed with the community and not very critical of its flaws. Even if you don't join, leaving the group with a positive feeling about itself is a nice thing to do."

Don't be surprised, by the way, if we ask questions too!

So you've got through your first visit. (Sometimes it's possible for a first visit to be extended, but please don't count on it.) We hope you've had an interesting, stimulating and enjoyable time. Perhaps you now have a better idea of what you're looking for. If you want to visit us again, we'll want to discuss this amongst ourselves. If you seemed to us to fit in reasonably well, we'll invite you to come again, probably for a couple of weeks. And then we advise anyone thinking of asking to join us to visit a few other communities first in order to gain perspective. If a community doesn't want you to return, this could be for any number of reasons. I'd advise you to try not to take it too personally, and to keep on looking for one where you will fit in.

How you go about joining different communities again varies quite a lot: some you have to buy your way into; others are looking for particular skills. Most, if not all, are looking for people they feel they can live with; and most have a trial period during which everyone concerned has a chance to assess how it might work out. We have a relatively short period of six weeks to cause minimum disruption and to get the pain over with. (It can be painful being

a prospective member, but again, remember we've all been through it.) When the trial period is up you'll have to ask yourself whether or not this is what you really want, and the community will have to decide whether or not they want to live with you. Some communities make more of this decision than others and it can be a difficult time for all concerned. If you're accepted, you can always change your mind and leave, but those already there are making a decision which they'll have no power to reverse. Some may have cause to regret decisions they made in the past.

Perhaps it would be wonderful if we could have ever-open doors and admit anyone who wanted to be here for however long they wanted. But although communal life can bring out the best in some people, others really aren't suited to it. And it's important for us to be able to feel that we're all committed, not only to the place but also to each other. This is with the hope that when the going gets tough, either for individuals or for the place as a whole, the difficulties aren't greater than they need be. Don't be disheartened - many people have been through it and survived! I certainly hope I haven't put you off. As I've said, visiting communities can be a stimulating and enjoyable experience, and how are you going to find out what they're like, or if you're suited to living in one, unless you give it a try?

Good luck!

This article is reprinted, in an edited form, from Diggers and Dreamers 1992/93.

Community Self Build

" ... building is work for the future, work for others who stand outside of the community that you know. In this sense, all building is a gift to others, but it can be executed either in the spirit of gift or obligation. Although the work is given to the future, the effect of that gift is to build and hold communities together." Christopher Day, Building with Heart.

*I*n the 1970s and 80s the typical image of a communal building was a large ramshackle mansion in various stages of disrepair, being held together with communal willpower and ingenuity. Maintainance weeks abounded where every available member and visitor, who knew one end of a pointing trowel from another, was pressed into active service to stop the communal rot and plug the leaky roof. One or two communities tackled major renovation projects, or used the skills gained in working on their own property to do building work locally.

But very few ventured into building new purpose built communal buildings tending to expand around the edges using caravans etc. In the late 1980s that situation started to change with a number of new and existing groups starting to use enviromentally friendly building techniques to provide new purpose built accommodation and community buildings for their members. Notable amongst these were the Lightmoor project (see Article p9), Findhorn in Scotland and the work carried out at The Centre For Alternative Technology in conjunction with the Walter Segal Trust.

The Walter Segal Self-build Trust is a charity which offers information, advice, support and training to people, especially those in housing need and on low incomes, to enable them to build decent homes for themselves and their families. The Trust, set up in 1988, initiated a three year development programme intended to foster and support self-build groups throughout Britain. This is currently being achieved by co-ordinating potential self builders, community groups, sympathetic local authorities and other landowners, building societies and other financial institutions in order to create a network of self-build groups and support agencies. The trust now has the beginings of its regional network established and has recently published the first comprehensive guide to self-build for those in housing need.

The, so-called, Segal method of building is simple, flexible and can be used by anyone (even those with no previous building or DIY experience) to produce an attractive and comfortable house, which can be designed to the self-builder's individual needs. Among those who have designed and built their own homes in this way are people on council waiting lists, a woman single parent, and men and women near retirement age. Unlike more conventional methods of construction, the Segal method imposes no specific timetable or uniform design, and allows people to

Building Green at Findhorn

In 1990 the Findhorn Foundation started constructing the ecological village. The task is huge, as their aim in not only to replace old caravans with ecological houses but also to create a village whose whole purpose is to show a way of life based on respect for the earth and the spiritual principles of the Findhorn Foundation. Over the next few years they will be building more houses for Community members, accommodation for visitors and communal buildings: they intend to expand their renewable energy systems, provide ecological sewage systems and continue to develop techniques in ecological construction.

A book - *Simply Build Green* (by John Talbot) - about the ecological houses at Findhorn and the techniques used in building them is available from: Phoenix Mail Order, The Park, Forres IV36 OTZ. Price £24.95 plus p&p.

build their houses individually, co-operating where they wish or need to. It allows steeply sloping sites and poor quality ground to be utilised, and enables buildings to be fitted into the landscape without major site works or enviromental damage. The Segal Method is based on a post-and-beam timber frame into which readily available material such as plasterboard are fixed. Simple 'dry' joints can be made with bolts and screws. This method has many advantages:

• It can be mastered quickly by anyone without building experience.

• It is economical and little work needs to be done by sub-contractors.

• Because the buildings are raised above the ground on posts, the foundations can be reduced to a minimum and it is not necessary to level the site in the usual way. It becomes possible to develop difficult sites with steep slopes, or poor ground, eco-nomically.

• One or two-storey homes of almost any layout can be constructed and because the walls are non-load bearing the layout can even be changed as work progresses.

• Extensions can easily be added at a later stage.

• The method relies on simple but comprehensive information to build from. This includes layout plans, diagrams of the structure, details showing how the parts join together, a detailed list of all instructions. This information is provided by an architect familiar with the Segal Method.

The move to self/new build communities is partly due to the spiralling of house prices during the 1980s, but also perhaps due to a growing realisation of the difficulties, in terms of energy conservation, costs of maintanance/restoration and inappropriate design, posed by large rambling houses.

See Directory entries number 15, 18, 28, 48 and 78 for details of communities involved in self/new-build.

The Walter Segal Trust Give free advice and assistance to people who wish to build their own homes. This advice covers such matters as: how to establish a scheme; the costs involved and the financial options available. They organise seminars and practical training courses. There is a demonstration 'low energy' house built in the Segal manner at the Centre for Alternative Technology in Wales.

Contact *Mike Daligan, Walter Segal Self-build Trust, Room 212, Panther House, 38 Mount Pleasant, London WC1X 0AP. ☎ 071 833 4152.*

Produce a complete information pack for people in housing need who want to build their own homes *You Build: A Guide to Building Your Own Home* by Ross Fraser and Steve Platt. It costs £16 for the pack of 6 booklets, or £3.50 for each separate booklet. Prices include postage and packing.

"Nobody will ever be able to tell me that I cannot do something - anything. Ever again."

Segal Self-builder

"So we can bring back the joy of building and thereby make people happier."

Walter Segal, Architect

Good Guru Guide

*W*e doubt if many of the communities listed in Diggers & Dreamers will insist that you break all ties with the outside world before you can join but in a "post-Waco" environment one can never be too careful! So before transferring the contents of your bank account to a guru-dominated commune try this "guru rating system" devised by the Institute for Social Inventions. They say that the total of 'yes' answers to the following questions can provide a rough-and-ready comparative rating.

1   Is what the guru offers free?
2   Is the guru relatively poor? ie not having personal control (or control in practice) over more wealth than

is needed for him or her to live in normal comfort and dignity?
3   Is it unnecessary to join the organisation in order to have access to the teachings?
4   Is it easy to leave the guru; are ex-disciples treated satisfactorily; and are 'opponents' of the guru treated fairly?
5   Does the guru refrain from sexual involvement with the disciples?
6   Is free contact allowed with families and friends?
7   Is there respect for quality in the work of the guru's organisation?
8   Are the guru's words in harmony with past spiritual insights?
9   Is the organisation non-authoritarian - are there signs of democracy, for instance, or of questioning and debate and thinking for oneself being welcomed?

10 Is the guru's legitimacy anchored in a tradition that points back to previous gurus, rather than the guru claiming to be the sole arbiter of his or her legitimacy?

11 Does the guru avoid claiming to be a perfect master offering the only route to enlightenment? Is he open about his own 'feet of clay', if he has them?

13 Does the guru's organisation, in its methods and in all aspects of its daily regime, successfully avoid psychologically coercive or brain-washing-style techniques?

14 Do the guru's or organisation's replies to these questions agree with evidence from other sources?

15 Does the guru have less than 1,000 signed-up disciples (Gurus with large followings seem to be more prone to succomb to the temptations of power!)

Apparently Krishnamurti comes out of this very well, with Swami Bhaktivedanta of the Hare Krishna movement not far behind! Low scorers include Bhagwan (Osho) and Maharishi!

Glossary

Co-operative *A legal entity (often registered with the Registrar of Friendly Societies as a limited liability Industrial and Provident Society) which can own property, make contracts etc. A co-op is distinct from its members. Although they control it they may not divide its assets between them (privately made loans would obviously be repaid however). Each member has one share (and consequently one vote) and money invested is lent as 'loan stock'. This contrasts with the more conventional Company Limited by Shares where shares held (and consequently voting power) bear a direct relationship to financial investment.*

Co-operative Development Agency *Usually a local independent voluntary organisation with paid workers which primarily promotes worker co-ops and helps people set them up. Some CDAs give assistance to housing co-ops as well but this will often depend on the remit which they have been given by their funder(s).*

Collective *A living or working group who have chosen to do things co-operatively. They may or may not have a legal structure.*

Commune, Community, Communal group, Intentional Community *Used interchangeably for a group of people who have chosen to live together.*

Sometimes a group uses the word 'community' to express a more individualistic lifestyle than 'commune' suggests. Sometimes 'community' is used to avoid the prejudices arising from the bad press image of communes in the 1960s, as bunches of lazy, drug crazed hippies!

Consensus *Consensus decision making is different from voting. It involves finding a decision that everyone can live with, if necessary by modifying the original proposal to take objections into account. The aim of this kind of decision making is agreement rather than the competitive victory of voting.*

Facilitator *A key rôle in meetings. The facilitator does not run the meeting like a chairperson but is rather the servant of the meeting. S/he takes responsibility for smooth running, drawing out proposals for decisions, encouraging everyone to participate and helping the group to achieve its aims for the meeting.*

Housing Co-operative *A Co-operative (see above) in which all tenants are eligible to become members. In England and Wales property cannot be owned jointly by more than four individuals. This and other (usually ideological) factors lead most communes and communities to register as housing co-ops.*

Income Sharing *Members put all the money they earn individually and in any collective projects into the* commune. Some groups share a part of their income only. In others individuals pay a fixed contribution towards the commune's expenses.

LETS *Local Economic Trading System. A sophisticated local bartering system which allows people to acquire or sell goods and services without traditional cash. In concept, a LETS System combines some features of a credit card and a barter system. In practice, a LETS System is a computer program which helps needers and providers find each other while also maintaining an accounting of the non-cash component of each transaction.*

Legal Framework/Legal Structure *A legally recognised form of group identity, eg a registered co-op, limited company, trust or charity. The rules or constitution set down the rights and responsibilities of the group towards the individual and of the individual towards the group.*

Living Groups *Often used to refer to small subgroups within a large community. Living groups may cook and eat together or may be more of a social or emotional support group or may even share all aspects of living together. The phrase is less often used to refer to a communal group.*

Organic Horticulture *A sustainable system of farming and gardening which uses crop rotation, compost-*ing, green manuring and biological controls rather than artificial fertilizers and pesticides.

Permaculture *A design system for sustainable human habitats using natural ecosystems, traditional farming methods and modern science and technology.*

Prospective Member, Provisional Member *Someone who is living in a community intending to become a member after an initial trial period (often called provisional membership). Some communes have a fixed length of time (one to six months), others are more flexible or have no provisional membership at all.*

Self Sufficiency *Usually means growing enough vegetables to feed everyone in the commune without buying any in. Also used more widely to cover other kinds of food, eg eggs, milk, meat, grain. Also used even more widely to mean the group produces as much as possible of what it needs. This is also called 'self reliance' and can include having a self managed income source (ie a collective business).*

Skill Sharing *Teaching skills, especially practical ones, to others in order to equalise opportunity, power and responsibility.*

Worker Co-operative *A Co-operative (see above) in which all workers are eligible to become members.*

Useful Books

GENERAL

ABRAMS, P and McCULLOCH, A (1976) *Communes, Sociology and Society* Cambridge University Press, Cambridge

AGASI, Y and DARON,Y (eds) (1982) *Alternative Way of Life, The: the First International Conference on Communal Living* Kibbutz Movement

ANSELL, V et al (eds) (1989) *Diggers and Dreamers - The 1990/91 Guide to Communal Living* Communes Network, Sheffield

BARKER, E (1989) *New Religious Movements: A Practical Introduction* HMSO, London

BENNET, J G (1977) *Needs of a New Age Community* Coombe Springs Press, Gloucester

BERGER, B M (1981) *The Survival of a Counter-culture: Ideological Work and Everyday Life among Rural Communards* University of California Press, London

BETTELHIEM, B *Children of the dream - Children in Kibbutz* Paladin, London.

BIRCHALL, J (1988) *Building Communities the Co-operative Way* Routledge & Kegan Paul, London

BOOKCHIN, M *The Philosophy of Social Ecology*

BOROWSKI, K (1984) *Attempting an Alternative Society: A Sociological Study of a Selected Communal Revitalisation Movement in the USA* Norwood Editions, Norwood

CALLENBACH, E (1978) *Ecotopia* Pluto Press, London

COATES, C et al (eds) (1991) *Diggers and Dreamers 92/93* Communes Network, Milton Keynes

COHN, N (1970) *The Pursuit of the Millenium: Revolutionary MIllenarians and Mystical Anarchism of the Middle Ages* Oxford

DUNN, N *Living Like I Do* Futura, London

FAIRFIELD, R (1972) *Communes Europe* Alternative Foundations

FITZGERALD, F (1986) *Cities on a hill* Picador, London

GIRARDET, H (ed) (1976) *Land for the People* Crescent Books, London

GORMAN, C (1975) *People Together* Paladin, London

HARDY, D (1991) *From New Towns to Green Politics* Spon, London

HARPER, C (1989) *Grafic Guide to Anarchy* Grafic Books, London

HOSTETLER, J A (1974) *Hutterite Society* John Hopkins University Press, Baltimore

HOURIET, R (1971) *Getting Back Together* Abacus, London

JAMES, J (1980) *Atlantis Alive* Caliban, London

JAMES, J (1980) *Atlantis Is ...* Caliban, London

JUDSON, J (1974) *Families of Eden: Communes and the New Anarchism* Seabury Press, New York

KANTER, R M (1972) *Commitment and Community: Communes and Utopias in Sociological Perspective* Harvard University Press, Cambridge Massachusetts

KANTER, R M (1979) *Communes in Cities* from 'Co-ops, Communes and Collectives' edited by CASE and TAYLOR; pp 112-135

KANTER, R M (1973) *Communes: creating and managing the collective life* Harper & Row, New York

KINKADE, K (1973) *A Walden Two Experiment: the first five years of Twin Oaks* Morrow

KOMAR, I *Living the Dream* Twin Oaks, Virginia

Le GUIN, U K *The Disposessed* New York

McCARTHY, M (1950) *A Source Of Embarrassment* Heinemann, London

McLAUGHLIN, C and DAVIDSON, G (1985) *Builders of the Dawn* Sirius, Massachusetts

MELVILLE, K (1972) *Communes in the Counter-culture* Munro & Co

MERCER, J (1984) *Communes: A Social History and Guide* Prism Press, Dorchester

PEPPER, D (1991) *Communes and the Green Vision* Green Print, London

POPENOE, C and O (1984) *Seeds of Tomorrow: New Age Communities that Work* Harper and Row, New York

RAJAN, V ed *Rebuilding Communities: Experiences and Experiments in Europe* Green Books, Totnes

RIDDELL, C (1990) *The Findhorn Community - Creating a human identity for the 21st Century* Findhorn Press, Forres

RIGBY, A (1974) *Alternative Realities: a study of communes and their members* Routledge & Kegan Paul, London.

RIGBY, A (1974) *Communes in Britain* Routledge & Kegan Paul, London

RIVERS, P (1975) *The Survivalists* Eyre Methuen, London.

ROBERTS, R E (1971) *The New Communes: Coming Together in America* Prentice Hall, New Jersey

SOCIETY OF BROTHERS, THE (1963) *Children in Community* Plough Publishing House, New York

SUNDANCER, E (1973) *Celery Wine: the story of a country commune* Community Publication Co-op

WARD, C (1985) *When We Build Again, Let's Have Housing That Works!* Pluto, London

WOOD, A (1988) *Greentown: a case study of a proposed Alternative Community* Energy and Environment Research Unit Occasional Paper no. EERU 057, Open University, Milton Keynes

ZABLOCKI, B (1973) *The Joyful Community: An Account of the Bruderhof - A Communal Movement in its Third Generation* Penguin, Baltimore

ZICKLIN, G (1983) *Counter-cultural Communes: A Sociological Perspective* Greenwood Press, London

UTOPIAS

ARMYTAGE, W H G (1961) *Heavens Below: Utopian experiments in Britain 1560 - 1960* Routledge & Kegan Paul, London

ASPLER, A (1974) *Communes Through the Ages* Julian Messner, New York

BEECHER & BIENVENU, H (1972) *The Utopian Vision of Charles Fourier* Beacon Press

BESTOR, A (1950) *Backwoods Utopias: the Sectarian and Owenite Phases of Communitarian Socialism in America, 1663-1829* Pennsylvania

FOGARTY, R S (1980) *Directory of American Communal and Utopian History* Greenwood Press, London

GARNETT, R G (1972) *Co-operation and The Owenite Socialist Communities in Britain 1825-45* Manchester University Press

GIDE, C (1930) *Communist and Co-operative Colonies* Harrap, London

GOODWIN, B (1978) *Social Science and Utopias: Nineteenth Century Models of Social Harmony* Harvester Press, Sussex

HARDY, D (1979) *Alternative Communities in Ninetenth Century England* Longmans, London

HARDY, D and WARD, C (1984) *Arcadia for All: The Legacy of a Makeshift Landscape* Mansell, London & New York

HARRISON, J F C (1969) *Robert Owen and the Owenites in Britain and America: The quest for the New Moral World* Routledge & Kegan Paul, London

HAYDEN, D (1976) *Seven American Utopias* MIT Press, London

HOLLOWAY, M (1966) *Heavens On Earth: Utopian Communities in America 1680-1880* Dover, New York

HOSTETLER, J A (1974) *Communitarian Societies* Holt, Rinehart & Winston, New York

KROPOTKIN, P (1919) *Fields,factories and workshops* Nelson & Sons

KROPOTKIN, P (1902/4) *Mutual Aid* Heinemann, London

KROPOTKIN, P (1926) *The Conquest of bread* Vanguard Press

MARSHALL, P (1992) *Demanding the Impossible: The History of Anarchism* Harper Collins, London

MARSHALL, P (1992) *Nature's Web: An exploration of ecological thinking* Simon & Schuster, London

MORRIS, W (1890) *News from Nowhere* London

MUMFORD, L (1959) *The Story of Utopias* New York

NORDOFF, C (1966) *The Communalistic Societies of America* Dover Publications, New York

NOYES, J H (1966) *Strange cults and Utopias of 19th century America* Dover Publications, New York

QUAIL, J *The Slow Burning Fuse - The lost history of British Anarchy* Paladin, London

REXROTH, K (1975) *Communalism: from its origins to the Twentieth Century* Peter Owen, London.

SHAW, N (1935) *A Colony in the Cotswolds* Daniel, London

TOLSTOY, L (1899) *What is to be done?* Crowell, London

WHITWORTH, J K (1975) *Gods Blueprint: A Sociological Study of Three Utopian Sects* Routledge and Kegan Paul, London.

WILSON, B (1970) *Religious Sects: A Sociological Study* Weidenfeld & Nicolson, London

PRACTICAL

ALBERY, N (ed) (1992) *Book of Visions* Virgin Books

ALEXANDER, C et al (1977) *Pattern Language* Oxford University Press, New York

AUVINE, B et al (1981) *A Handbook for Consensus Decision-making: Building United Judgement Center for Conflict Resolution* Madison

BELL, G *The Permaculture Way*

BRADSHAW, J (1988) *Guide to House Buying, Selling and Conveyancing* Castle Books, Leamington Spa

BROOME J and RICHARDSON, B *The Self-Build Book*

COCKERTON , P and WHYATT, A (1980) *The Workers Co-operative Handbook* ICOM Co-publications, London

COCKERTON, P (1988) *A Handbook for Secretaries of Co-operatives* ICOM Co-publications, London

COOVER, V; DEACON, E; ESSEN, C and MOORE, C (1981) *Resource Manual for a Living Revolution* Movement for a New Society, Philadelphia

DARROW, K and SAXENIAN, M *Appropriate Technology Source Book: A guide to practical books for village & small community technology*

ENO, S and TREANOR, D (1982) *Collective Housing Handbook* Laurieston Hall Publications

INGHAM, A *Self Help House Repairs Manual* Penguin, London

JELFS, M (1982) *Manual for Action: Techniques to enable groups engaged in Action for Change* Action Resources

JELFS, M (1984) *Mortgage Finance for Housing Co-operatives* Empty Property Unit, London

MacFARLANE, R (1986) *Financial Planning and Control* ICOM Co-publications, London.

RANDALL, R (1980) *Co-operative and Community Dynamics: Or your meetings don't have to be that bad!* Barefoot Books

RURAL RESETTLEMENT GROUP, THE (1984) *The Rural Resettlement Handboook* Prism Alpha, Sherbourne

STEAD (1980) *Self Build Housing Groups and Co-operatives: Ideas in Practice* Anglo German Foundation

STEPHENS, David *The Survivor House*

TRAINING/ACTION AFFINITY GROUP (1979) *Building Social Change Communities* Movement for a New Society, Philadelphia

TREANOR, D (1987) *Buying Your Home with Other People* NFHA and Shelter, London

Useful Addresses

NETWORKS

Camphill Village Trust Delrow House, Hilfield Lane, Aldenham, Hertfordshire WD2 8DJ. ☎ 0923 856006. *The Camphill Movement was begun 50 years ago by a group inspired by the work of educationalist and philosopher Rudolf Steiner. The movement encompasses 30 centres in Britain and another 42 worldwide. As well as curative education for children with special needs, the Camphill Village Trust builds communities together with adults who have special needs. In all Camphill communities daily life is shared in extended families of people with different abilities. Recreational life is rich and varied, with a Christian spiritual basis. Satisfying and useful practical work is provided for all. Each centre derives its income from sales of produce, DSS benefits and other grants. Neither the co-workers nor villagers receive a wage. Instead, each person has their needs met by the community.*

Communes Network care of Diggers and Dreamers.

Confederation of Co-operative Housing (CCH) care of Diggers and Dreamers. *Nothing has replaced the National Federation of Housing Co-operatives since it disappeared at the end of*

1991. However, a steering group has been formed to guide the creation of a new national alliance of local federations of housing co-ops - the CCH.

Edward Carpenter Community Trust care of 37 Ritherdon Road, London SW17 8QE. ☎ 081 672 8857. *Network of gay men ultimately seeking to form one or more gay men's rural community(ies).*

Emissary Foundation International Mickleton House, Mickleton, Gloucestershire GL55 6RY. ☎ 0386 438251. *A worldwide network of spiritual communities in Canada, USA, France, South Africa as well as Mickleton in England. See Directory Entry 47.*

Friends of the Western Buddhist Order (FWBO) London Buddhist Centre, 51 Roman Road, London E2 0HU. ☎ 081 981 1225. *An organisation offering the teaching and practice of Buddhism in a way suited to people living in industrialised countries. There are meditation and retreat centres and classes. The FWBO has a number of communities around the world, including many in Britain, offering a supportive environment for spiritual practice and a chance to deepen friendships. There are also many "right livelihood" businesses where members work co-operatively to offer something to society.*

Hutterian Brethren Darvell Bruderhof, Robertsbridge, East Sussex TN32 5DR. ☎ 0580 880626. *There are Bruderhof Communities in the USA, Germany and Britain. They publish a magazine, The Plough, which is dedicated to all who work for a personal transformation in Christ and a radical turn from the materialism, militarism, racism and impurity of this world, looking toward the coming of God's Kingdom here on earth. Visitors are welcome at all Bruderhof communities by previous written arrangement. See Directory Entry 23.*

L'Arche 10 Briggate, Silsden, Keighley, Yorkshire BD20 9JT. ☎ 0535 656186. *See Directory Entry 19.*

National Association of Christian Communities and Networks (NACCAN) Woodbrooke, 1046 Bristol Road, Selly Oak, Birmingham B29 6LJ.

☎ 021 472 8079. *NACCAN seeks to support and represent its members and promote and encourage the growth of the Christian community movement and the renewal of society. They believe that small groups can bring about change and that this can come about in many different ways. Members come from established religious orders and new communities, local churches, individuals and networks. The office, based at Woodbrooke, the Quaker college in Birmingham, is staffed by volunteers who will do their best to answer any queries. Publications include* Christian Community *magazine and a directory of Christian communities, groups and networks; there are area meetings and an annual assembly. The office holds a great deal of useful information about communities, groups and networks. Please phone or write if you wish to visit.*

National Federation of Housing Associations (NFHA) 175 Gray's Inn Road, London WC1X 8UP. ☎ 071 278 6571. *NFHA is the central representative and negotiating body for housing associations, providing advice to associations and publishing the monthly magazine* Voluntary Housing *and* Association Weekly, *as well as a number of useful books and pamphlets on matters of concern to housing associations and their tenants.*

Powwow Box 7, 124 Vassall Road, London SW9 6JB. *A newsletter primarily about village scale alternative communities worldwide.*

Radical Routes 25a Stanley Road, Manchester M16 8HS. ☎ 061 232 9094. *See Directory Entry 63.*

Social Ecology Network care of Diggers and Dreamers. *Works towards local self-reliance and local self-management through ideas and projects which integrate community and ecology.*

Soul Families International Network care of Diggers and Dreamers. *Love groups to share truth, lives and unconditional love. Caring communication and communion at all levels,* real community for spiritually self-aware people. Liberation of body, mind and soul for transcendental ecstacy, creativity and human service. Non profit, non sectarian. Life Science workshops and home-study training courses (holistic training for the total person; empowerment of the individual and the group at every level; co-operation for creative problem solving; leadership training for personal and social change; improved communication with oneself and others; understanding the laws of life and attunement to the evolutionary plan) also available. Plus "life-seeing" tours of India for people with social, spiritual and cultural interests. They ask you to write frankly and in detail enclosing an sae or two IRCs.

PROFESSIONAL

DOR (Northern) Insurance Ltd 36a London Road, Alderley Edge, Cheshire SK9 7DZ. ☎ 0625 582530. *Registered insurance brokers specialising in housing associations.*
Ecology Building Society 18 Station Road, Cross Hills, Keighley, West Yorkshire BD20 7EH. ☎ 0535 35933. *Useful and responsible place to bank your spare funds till you need them. Also a source of loans.*
Housing Corporation 149 Tottenham Court Road, London W1P 0BN. ☎ 071 387 9466. *Statutory body responsible to the Secretary of State for the Environment, who appoints the members of its Board. It is the primary source of funding for housing associations, and is responsible for supervising and controlling housing associations registered with it.*
Industrial Common Ownership Finance plc (ICOF) 12-14 Gold Street, Northampton NN1 1RS. ☎ 0604 37563. *Source of finance for workers co-operatives.*
Industrial Common Ownership Movement (ICOM) Vassalli House, 20 Central Road, Leeds LS1 6DE. ☎ 0532 461737/8 ⌨! *National federation of worker co-ops. Also provides registration service for organisations*

wanting "unusual" structures.
Janet Slade & Co Fourways House, 57 Hilton Street, Manchester, M1 2EJ. ☎ 061 236 1493. *Chartered Accountants specialising in work with co-ops, charities and voluntary organisations.*
Malcolm Lynch Vassalli House, 20 Central Road, Leeds LS1 6DE. ☎ 0532 429600 ⌨! *Solicitor specialising in work with co-ops.*
Mercury Provident plc Orlingbury House, Lewes Road, Forest Row, East Sussex RH18 5AA. ☎ 0342 823739. *A Steiner based organisation which lends to socially useful projects that have support from the wider community.*
National and Provincial Building Society Commercial Lending Dept, Provincial House, Bradford BD1 1NL. ☎ 0274 733444.
Nationwide Building Society Public Sector Lending Unit, Kings Park Road, Moulton Park, Northampton NN3 1NL. ☎ 0604 495353.
Rural Development Commission 141 Castle Street, Salisbury, Wiltshire SP1 3TP. ☎ 0722 336255.
Scottish Co-operative Development Committee (SCDC) Templeton Business Centre, Templeton Street, Bridgeton, Glasgow G40 1DE. ☎ 041 554 3797.
Simon Erskine & Co 14a Downshire Hill, Hampstead, London NW3 1NR. ☎ 071 435 4484. *Accountancy practice specialising in work with housing co-operatives.*
Sinclair Taylor & Martin 9 Thorpe Close, Portobello Road, (Cambridge Gardens), London W10 5XL. ☎ 081 969 3667. *Solicitor specialising in work with co-ops and charities.*
Small Firms Service ☎ 100 ask for Freefone Enterprise.
Walter Segal Self Build Trust Room 212, Panther House, 38 Mount Pleasant, London WC1X 0AP. ☎ 071 833 4152.

OTHER

Commonweal Collection care of J B Priestley Library, University of Bradford, Bradford, West Yorkshire BD7 1DP. ☎ 0274 733404. *A library devoted to non-violence and social change, which includes books on* alternative lifestyles. Whilst serving mainly students and researchers, the collection is open to anyone.

Community Building in Britain care of Angela Faria, 125 Greenham Road, Newbury, Berkshire RG14 7JE. *A growing network of volunteers from all walks of life and many parts of the country, who meet regularly to 'build community'. The work is based on the ideas described in Dr M Scott Peck's book,* The Different Drum, *and further developed by the Foundation for Community Encouragement (FCE) in Connecticut, USA. Since 1990 they have successfully sponsored a series of workshops, each led by facilitators from the Foundation, with whom close links are maintained. However, they continue to go their own way in creating an independent network and organisation, seeking to work alongside FCE. Their major project at present is to train leaders from this country.*

Cult Information Service BCM Cults, London WC1N 3XX. ☎ 081 651 3322.

Education Otherwise PO Box 120, Leamington Spa, Warwickshire CV32 7ER. *Movement for de-schooling children and promoting home education.*

Family Information and Rescue (FAIR) BCM Box 3535, PO Box 12, London WC1N 3XX. ☎ 081 539 3940. *FAIR offers counselling and support to parents of young adults who have joined religious cults. FAIR's Helpline number is 0482 443104.*

Hospitality Exchange 116 Coleridge Street, San Francisco, California 94110, USA. *A network/directory of friendly travel-oriented people who have agreed to offer each other hospitality when travelling. Only people listed in the directory may use the service.*

Information Network Focus On Religious Movements (INFORM) Houghton Street, London WC2A 2AE. ☎ 071 955 7654. *Studies cults and religious movements.*

Institute for Social Inventions 20 Heber Road, London NW2 6AA. ☎ 081 208 2853. *Publishes a regular newsletter featuring innovative (non nuts and bolts) ideas for making the world a better place.*

International Voluntary Service Old Hall, East Bergholt, Colchester, Essex CO7 6TG. ☎ 0206 298215. *A pacifist organisation, running one to three week workcamps for anyone over 18. Several held in communities or other co-operative ventures in Britain and across the world.*

LETS Link UK 61 Woodcock Road, Warminster, Wiltshire BA12 9DH. ☎ 0985 217871. *National co-ordination for local LETS schemes throughout Britain.*

People for Action 44 Bradford Street, Birmingham B5 6HX. ☎ 021 622 2747. *People for Action's members are housing associations which are working to empower local communities and regenerate local economies. They link investment in social housing with jobs, training opportunities and infrastructure improvements.*

Permaculture Association PO Box 1, Buckfastleigh, Devon TQ11 0LH. ☎ 03643 333.

Quaker International Social Projects (QISP) Friends House, Euston Road, London W1. ☎ 071 387 3681 x2255. *Organise international work camps.*

Recharge 33 Barons Court Road, Penylan, Cardiff CF3 7DG. ☎ 0222 481369. *A group set up to understand burnout and its remedies. Courses deal with both internal and external factors of burnout, and with support structures, assertiveness training, co-counselling, various therapies and relaxation techniques. Recharge only runs such courses in Cardiff at the moment but would like to grow.*

Servas PO Box 1035, Edinburgh EH3 9JQ. *Network of hosts and travellers which provides a way in which people can further world peace by exchanging hospitality.*

Working Weekends on Organic Farms (WWOOF) 19 Bradford Road, Lewes, East Sussex BN7 1RB. *Publish a newsletter and organise voluntary work weekends for members. A good way of visiting communities.*

International Addresses

This brief listing of communal groups is compiled almost entirely from recent information given to us by the groups themselves, or by another group in their country. It has been exciting and inspiring to receive such a long stream of friendly letters and interesting brochures.

Do let us know if any of our info is wrong, or if you know of communities we haven't listed.

In some cases fuller listings were given in the 92/93 edition, and in particular we reproduced a long list of Brazilian groups, but we have been unable to confirm the existence of these communities. After the few unconfirmed groups we've listed, we've placed the symbol ✳.

Organisations who can give more information about communal living in their country are shown with the symbol ⓘ.

If you are thinking of visiting any of these groups, please remember that they are people's homes. Write to them first, and wait for them to invite you. Note that some communities may take a while to reply to your letters, and some may not be open to visitors at the moment. It is a courtesy to include an International Reply Coupon, although these are quite expensive to buy.

We hope that this list will help increase communication between existing communities, and be a valuable resource for people thinking of setting up new ones. Good luck with your searching. You will find a world of many exciting possibilities.

EUROPE

Austria

ⓘ **Mag. Friedrich Köstlinger** Frauendorf 76, A-3710 Ziersdorf. *Write in English or German. They have a list of about 20 communities in Austria, which they will send you if you write showing real interest. They ask us to include this: "Dear contact-seeking friend, Austria is said to be the Isle of the Blessed. If you want to let your life be blessed by the LOVE which created this world, come and see, and share your life with one of the Austrian communities."*

Franziskusgemeinschaft Am Kalvarienberg 5, A-7423 Pinkafeld. *"Family monastery": farming and gardening. Contact with Third World.*

Schule des Friedens (School of Peace) A-3914 Loschberg. *International peace work, alternative school, farming.*

Sonnenhof Ritterkamp 7, A-3911 Rappottenstein. *Small spiritual community. Unconditional love is the central theme of their being together.*

Wohngemeinschaft Nexenhof A-2042 Grund 100. *Humanist; therapy, bio-energetic gardening.*

••••••••••••••••••••••••••••••

Belgium

Antwerpen (N)

Gemeenschap van Ark (Jean Vamier) Jansseulei 12, B-2530 Boechout.

Brabant (Brussels area)

Colline de Pénuel Ferme de Louvrange, chemin de Vieusart 192, B-1300 Wavre. *Christian; support people in difficulties.*

Communauté du Goéland Le Goéland, rue Warichet 18, B-1401 Baulers. *Christian; linked to hostel for young women in difficulty.*

Communauté de la Poudrière rue de la Poudrière 60, B-1000 Bruxelles. *5 centres in Belgium (Brussels, Anderlecht, Vilvorde, Rummen &*

Péruwelz). Pluralist: open to all philosophies and religions.
De Regenboog Norbert Gillelaan 20, B-1070 Brussel. *Started 1974 elsewhere in Brussels; over the last few years have been 10-15 people: a small core group and several short and long term guests. "We try to live as a real community, sharing many things in daily life. And we are searching ways to live in real and practical solidarity with the poor and oppressed in the world."*

Namur (SE)

Rue de Borrel 7 Frizet, B-5003 St-Marc.

Liège (E)

Communauté St-François Acceuil St-François, Ayrifagne 3, B-4860 Pepinster. *Christian; lay / religious group.*
Les Matrognards rue Matrognard 11, B-4000 Liège. *Christian; young people; also called La Maison.*
Habitat Groupé de Sainte-Walburge rue Vieille Voie de Tongres 33, B-4000 Liège.
La Communauté Verte Voie Verte Voie 13, B-4660 Thimister. ☎ 087 44.65.05. *Started 1973; in 1993 6 adults & 5 children, in four families. Five flats, communal rooms on the ground floor and a large garden for growing communal food. Two communal meals a week, and two meetings a month. Providing an open space for socio-cultural alternatives and seeking another way of living together, to be a force for change in the region and to give birth to solidarity.*

•••••••••••••••••••••••••••••••••••

Denmark

ℹ **KoKoo** Rådhusstræde 13, DK-1466 København K. *This is the Danish Communes Association, set up in 1969. They run a matching service for communes looking for people and vice-versa, a free legal-aid service staffed by experts on housing legislation, and a magazine. Write in English, German or Swedish; they reply only in English. KoKoo have addresses of communes and families growing ecological and biodynamic vegetables who would like to hear from foreign people interested in their*

special growing method; visitors work 3-4 hours a day in return for free board and lodging.bout 10,000 Danish people live communally in some form, but the degree of communality has gone down. The average age of communards has gone up, but there is a younger generation coming up, based in urban squats.
ℹ **National Association for Sustainable Communities** (Landsforenigen for Økosamfund, abbreviated **LØS**) Gaia Villages, Skyumvej 101, DK-7752 Snedsted. *Founded in 1993 to represent, support, develop and inform on sustainable communities. 15 intentional communities were represented at the founding of the association, with focusses ranging between ecological, social and spiritual. Hope to facilitate the establishment of new communities, both urban and rural.*

Sjælland (Zealand)

Christiania Fristad DK-1407 København K.
Dragebjerggård Sonnerup, DK-3300 Frederiksværk. *Rural community.*
Hvalsolille Gården Knud Lavard Svej 96, DK-4174 Justrup.
Mørdrupgård Mørdrupvej 9, DK-3540 Lynge.
Svanholm Svanholm Gods, DK-4050 Skibby. *A large income-sharing group: about 75 adults and 60 children, in house groups; consensus decision-making; ecological farming.*

Fyn

Nyborg Efterskole Ringvej 5, DK-5800 Nyborg.
Stavnsbogården Orte Byvej 30, DK-5560 Årup.

Jylland (Jutland)

Andelssamfundet i Hjortshøj Lollandsgade 52, DK-8000 Århus C. *Suburban community.*
Andels-Samfundet Stationsstion 17, DK-8541 Skødstrup.
Århus-Klunserne Poppelgårdesvej 1, DK-8471 Sabro.
Baungården / Solibo Hover Kirkevej 49, DK-7100 Vejle.
Hjulby Spørring, DK-8380 Trige. *Suburban community.*

Jættestuen Herredsvejen 7, DK-8581 Nimtofte. *Not a community any more, but a family printing books. However they know a lot about communities and have a lot of contacts.*
Kirstinelund Skanderborgvej 132, Bjedstrup, DK-8600 Skanderborg. *Rural community.*
Mølle Skovly Lyngvej 21, DK-8832 Skals. *One family with a little chocolate factory.*
Nørremarksgården Hedelundsvej 30, Hvirring, DK-8762 Flemming.
Økologisk Landsbysamfund Torup Bygade 5, DK-3390 Hundested.

••••••••••••••••••••••••••••••••

Finland

Maailmankauppa (World Shop) Hietanimenkatu 10 D 3, 00100 Helsinki. ☎ 90-491 559. *Small Third World / Eco shop; also contact and information centre. Started 1981. 15 adults; 2 youngsters. Produce guide to responsible consuming. Promote walking, cycling and public transport. Info about ecological farms. Old name in Swedish was Miljöcentrum.*
Cultural-Ecological Club of Vanhakaupunki Viides linja 7 C 59, 00530 Helsinki. ☎ 90-701 6002. *Aims to repair old wooden house on wild uninhabited island near city centre. No electricity. Guests welcome to participate in voluntary work over the summer, or just to visit, but please contact them first.* •••••••••••••••••••••••••••

France

▣ **Réseaux-Espérance** 98 Boulevard des Rocs, F-86000 Poitiers. *Network: publishes a newsletter every three months; organises a festival every summer.*

Ile-de-France (Paris region)

Acceuil-Convention 52 rue Charles Baudelaire, F-93300 Aubervilliers. ☎ 48 34 27 81. *Welcomes people with pscyhological problems; linked to l'Orée below.*
Assise 40 rue Quincampoix (Esc. B, 1er étage), F-75004 Paris. *Centre for meditation and interior development.*
L'Orée 12 rue Ambroise Thomas, F92400 Courbevoie. ☎ 47 88 84 65.

Christian community of 23 adults and 25 children, with differing levels of investment in communal life. Members live in different houses; many income share. Work includes home education, a crèche, provision of retreat space, welcoming adults and children with psychological problems, a shop and a newsletter. Speaking and relating are important. Address also at Le Moulin, F-89120 Chêne-Arnoult (21 adults, 21 children).
Communauté de l'Arche de Jean Vannier 334 rue de Vaugirard, F75015 Paris.
Dis-Eco 31 rue A. Thomas, F-94200 Ivry-sur-Seine.
Emmaüs 2 ave. de la Liberté, F-94220 Charenton.
Lieux d'Acceuil Chaleureux (L.A.C.) 25 rue de Choisy, F-94400 Vitry-sur-Seine. *Founded from Emmaüs.*

Normandie (NW of Paris)

Communauté de Caulmont F-76400 Froberville. ☎ 35 27 31 72. *Ecumenical Christian community.*

Breizh/Bretagne (NW)

Communion de Boquen Association Culturelle de Boquen, Boite Postale 550, F-22010 St-Brieuc.
Communauté de la Poterie la Poterie, F-22980 Plélan-le-Petit.

Poitou-Charentes-Vendée (W)

Les Peupins Le Peu du Pin, F-79140 Le Pin. ☎ 49 81 03 99.
La Sepaye Chatenay, F-79150 Moutiers sous Argenton. ☎ 49 65 96 01.

Centre-Anjou (SW of Paris)

Communauté de Montsouris 26 rue de le Monnaie, F-45140 Ingré.
La Rebellerie F-49560 Nueil-sur-Layon.

Champagne-Lorraine (NE)

Communauté de Bois Gérard F-10130 Chessy-les-Prés. ☎ 25 70 67 09.
Ecolonie Thietry, F-88260 Hennezel. ☎ 29 07 00 27. *International ecology centre.*

Bourgogne-Franche-Comté (E)

Ferme-Acceuil Visargent, F-71330 Sens-sur-Seille. *Address unclear. Spirit of Communautés de l'Arche.*

Rhône-Alpes (inland SE)

Ardelaine Puausson, F-07190 St-Sauveur-de-Montagut.

Le Brousse F-07110 Vinezac-Largentiere.

Communauté du Surgeon 9 allée des Cardons, F-69120 Vaulx-en-Velin.

Domaine Agricole de Grignon Montfroc, F-26560 Séderon.

Ecolocal rue du Couvent, chemin du Rousselet, F-07140 Les Vans. *Ecology centre.*

Groupe de Lucinges Château, F-74380 Bonne.

Terre Nouvelle Eourres, F-26560 Séderon. ☎ 92 65 24 25. *5 Ad 5 Ch; similar in spirit to Findhorn. Each family lives separately; part of larger community of village (30 Ad, 15 Ch). Run a workshop/retreat centre. Not much visitor accommodation otherwise. Village is looking for more people with children and job or local activity who want to settle down on a long term basis.*

La Vigne F-38620 Velanne La Sauge. *Emissary Community.*

Auvergne-Limousin (inland S)

C.R.I.S.E. F-23340 Faux-la-Montagne.

Midi-Pyrénées (inland SW)

C.E.A. Saliens, F-09140 Seix.

Collectif du Casteru Banquiet, F-31480 Cadours.

Cun du Larzac route de St-Martin, F-12100 Millau. *Grew from successful campaign against army takeover of land. Cun is the Provençal word for wedge.*

Le Peyre Merigon, F-09230 Sainte-Croix-Volvestre.

Village 12 Le Serre, La Bastide l'Evêque, F-12200 Villefranche.

Languedoc-Roussillon (S)

Les Amis de la Douceur et de l'Harmonie El-Faitg, F-66230 Serralongue. ☎ 68 39 62 56.

Atelier du Jour Rue Principale, F-66320 Finestret.

Communauté de l'Abbaye de Lagrasse F-11220 Lagrasse.

Communauté de l'Arche La Borie Noble, F34260 Le Bousquet d'Orb. *The original Communauté de l'Arche, a group of communities founded on Gandhian principles. Also communities at: La Flayssière, 34650 Joncels; Nogaret, 34650 Roqueredonde; Les Truels de Larzac, 12100 Millau; Abbaye de Bonnecombe, 12120 Cassagnes-Bégonhès; Le Grand Mouligné, Montpezat-d'Agenais, 47360 Prayssas; La Grande Chouannière, Ségrie, 72170 Beaumont-sur-Sarthe; Bethsalem, Mas del Arca, Fenouillix, 66500 Prades; St-Antoine-l'Abbaye, 38160 St-Marcellin.*

Communauté du Moulin de l'Oulme F-30430 Rochegude. ☎ 66 24 42 11.

Le Coral F-30470 Aimargues. ☎ 66 88 00 12. *A community welcoming young people with psychological problems. Students studying psychology or social work may come and be part of the community for one to three months. They organise a network of other such "Lieux-de-Vie". Claude Sigala has written two books about le Coral, available from them for 50FF, Visiblement, je vous aime and Multiplicités.*

Permaculture Pyrénées Bouriège, F-11300 Limoux. *100 acres; forming group.*

Project Oasis Le Novis Haut, Vabres, F-30460 Lasalle.

La Val Dieu F-11190 Rennes-le-Chateau. ☎ 68.74.23.21. *Ancient Templar farm, set in 100 acres of forest and pasture. Offers accommodation to individuals and groups. Space for camping. Write or phone in advance. Enquiries in UK to Annette Toulson on 0225 311826.*

Provence-Alpes-Côte-d'Azur (SE)

Centre du Haut Saint Jean route de Pelleautier, F-05000 Gap.

Eourres BP 52, F-05300 Laragne.

Longo Maï BP 42, F-04300 Forcalquier. ☎ 92 73 05 98. Fax 92 73 18 18. *Started in 1973, with 30 people settling on 300 hectares on an abandoned mountainside. Now has over 150 active members and runs Radio Zinzine, a 24 hour free radio station, a visitors village and a music group. Co-operative living and working; economy based on agriculture, forestry, livestock, crafts. Co-founded*

CEDRI (European committee for the defence of refugees and immigrants), the European Civic Forum and the European Federation of Community Radios (FERL). Has established a farming co-op for refugees in Costa Rica. Now has six co-operative farms in France, one in Switzerland and one in Austria.
Le Souffle d'Or BP 3, F-05300 Barret le Bas.

••••••••••••••••••••••••••••••••

Germany

ⓘ **Ökodorf-Institut** Ginsterweg 3, DW-3074 Steyerberg. *"Advice for people in search of or wishing to establish a community. In our archives are lots of addresses of communities which don't want to be registered in an address list. The best is to visit us in our community, Lebensgarten Steyerberg (see Niedersachsen). Otherwise we would send a questionnaire to you for a long distance consultation."*

ⓘ **Eurotopia** Rieterstraße 5, D-8500 Nürnberg 90. *Journal of community living. European directory of community projects should be available by the time you read this.*

Berlin

Forum Kreuzberg Köpenickerstraße 174-175, D-1000 Berlin. *45 ad, 17 ch. Anthroposophical living, educational and working collective. Runs a people's college offering various courses.*
Synanon Bernburgerstraße 24, D-1061 Berlin. ☎ 030/250001-0. *Living without Drugs. Over 260 members, with four houses in Berlin and farmhouses in Hessen and Brandenburg. Three rules: no drugs, no power, no tobacco. Self-help group with no social workers, therapists or doctors. They run a removal and transport business, a printshop and a pottery in Berlin, and a pottery and biodynamic farming and gardening in Hessen.*
Ufa-Fabrik Viktoriastraße 10-18, D-1042 Berlin. ☎ 030/752 80 85 (10h-19h). *50 ad, 10 ch; free school, circus. Founded 1979. Monthly newsletter UFAZ available.*

Brandenburg (NE)
see Synanon, Berlin.

Schleswig-Holstein (far N)
Basisgemeinde Wulfshagenerhütten D-2303 Wulfshagenerhütten, Post Gettorf. ☎ 04346/5044. *Christian living and working collective. 70 people, singles and families, living in a old childrens home near Kiel. Seeking peace, justice and renewal.*

Niedersachsen (Hannover)
Energie und Umweltzentrum am Deister Am Elmchenbruch, D-3257 Springe-Eldagsen. ☎ 05044/380 or 1880. *20 ad, 7 ch; living in an old country schoolhouse; weekend seminars and educational holidays. Energy and environment centre.*
Klostergut in Heiningen D-3344 Heiningen. ☎ 05334/6971.
Kommune Niederkaufungen Kirchweg 1, D-3504 Kaufungen. ☎ 05605/2788 or 2702. *38 adults, 12 children; building; crafts, seminars. Socialist, income-sharing; communal education.*
Laurentiuskonvent Laurentiushof, D-3549 Wethen. *Christian; 40 adults: families and single people, mostly living in house groups. "Church and Peace."*
Lebensgarten Steyerberg Akazienhain 4, D-3074 Steyerberg. ☎ 05764/2370. *80 ad, 40 ch; spiritual focus; permaculture centre, bakery, healing centre, art and sound workshop, textile workshop, community-institute (advice for seeking and establishing communities).*
Lutter-Gruppe Auf der Domäne, D-3372 Lutter am Barenberge. *11 people living together in a strong anarchic collective; carpentry shop, bakery, architecture workshop, conference centre.*

Nordrhein-Westfalen (Cologne)
Sozialistische Selbsthilfe Köln SK Köln-Mitte, Salierring 37+41, D-5000 Köln. ☎ 0221 - 21 31 75. *A twenty year old community of people living in different houses, sharing money and goods: this is one of the contact addresses.*
Lernwerkstatt Niederstadtfeld Brunnenstraße 1, D-5531

Niederstadtfeld. ☎ 06596/551 or 1031. *Small group hoping to grow; eco-spirituality & eco-politics. Runs a conference centre.*
Michaelshof D-5231 Birnbach. *Bruderhof community.*

Hessen (Frankfurt, Kassel)
Kommune Riedmühle 1, D-6443 Alheim. *collective of 12 people. There is also a Synanon house in Hessen; see Berlin.*

Baden-Württemberg (SW)
Familie Hesselbach Hauptstraße 54, D-6761 Bisterschied. ☎ 06364/129. *14 ad, 5 ch; formed in 1982 with the amalgamation of a women's and a men's performing arts commune.*
Projekt Meiga Zeppelinstraße 7, D-7760 Radolfzell. ☎ 07732/56944 or 56932. *Sexuality and spirituality. Formed in 1978 as Bauhütte.*

Bayern / Bavaria
Eulenspiegel Gasthof Zum Eulenspiegel, Hauptstraße 99, D-8992 Wasserburg. ☎ 08382/6206. *Founded 1976; 10 people aged 5-74 (1990) running an inn, and producing a monthly newssheet Jedermensch. Meetings three times a week. Political anthroposophy.*
Goppinger Mühle Gemeinnützuge Arbeits- und Lebensgemeinschaft, D-8344 Egglhalm. ☎ 08543/894. *Mixed group living in an old watermill.*

●●●●●●●●●●●●●●●●●●●●●●●●●●●●●●●●

Greece
Harmonious Living Contact address: Bob Nadjemy, Harmonious Living, Griva 29, Halandri 15233, Athens. *Ashram just outside Athens, with about 12 members.*
Sarakiniko 28300 Vathi/Itaka. *35 people, incl children. Founded in 1979 from Germany. Grow olives, keep bees and goats. Monthly newsletter: Sarakiniko Einblick.*

●●●●●●●●●●●●●●●●●●●●●●●●●●●●●●●●

Ireland
An Droichead Beo Burtonport, Co. Donegal. ☎ 075 42030. *Alternative therapy centre and youth hostel. "An Droichead Beo is a large 18 roomed house. At present it is run by four young people. "We are all involved with Atlantis but at present we are a stepping stone or a contact point for the main group that has emigrated to South America. We are into alternative healing, crafts, magic, practical things like carpentry, building, gardening and decorating. There's plenty of room here for emotional expansion, and plenty of enjoyable, creative hard work. We are also open as a hostel for travellers. If you are interested in us, write or phone, or just turn up. As we are just starting out and our garden has yet to grow we would greatly appreciate any financial contributions that could be made. Hope to hear from you soon. P.S. we are also non-smoking vegetarians."*
An Meitheal Inch Island, Burnfoot, County Donegal. *Associated with Findhorn.*
Inisglas Trust Inisglas, Co. Wexford.

●●●●●●●●●●●●●●●●●●●●●●●●●●●●●●●●

Italy
Veneto (NE, Venice)
Gelso Verde Community via Chiooia 31, I-35100 Padova. ✳

Piemonte (NW, Turin)
Comunità dell' Arca Via Umberto I, n° 1, I-10080 Lugnacco, Torino.
Comunità di Damanhur via Pramarzo 3, I-10080 Baldissero Canavese, Torino. *A large spiritual community.*

Toscana (W, Florence/Pisa)
Aquarius Podere Poggio alle Fonti-Ciuciano, I-53037 San Gimignano (SI).
Community of Villa Vrindavana Via Comunale degli Scopeti 108, I-50026 San Casciano in Val di Pesa (Firenze).
Comune di Bagnaia podere Bagnaia, fraz. Ancaiano, I-53018 Sovicille (SI). ☎ 0577-311014. *An income sharing organic farming community of about 10 adults and 6 children. Founded 1979; raise animals, tend pastures, cereal crops, a vegetable garden, vines and olive trees; their whole economy is held in common. They would welcome visitors, a few at a time, from other communities, to exchange experiences and hospitality.*

Ecovillaggio Upacchi I-52030 Anghiari (AR). ☎ 0575-788195. *New ecovillage; most of their 100 members are building their houses, and some already live there; the village is growing from year to year.*

Elfi del Gran Burrone Loc. San Pellegrino, I-51020 Sambuca Pistoiese (PT).

Nomadelfia C.P. 178, I-58100 Grosseto. *About 300 people; Catholic; families adopt many abandoned children and adults; no money or private property.*

Osho Miasto I-53010 Frosini (SI). *Run spiritual growth workshops and host other visitors.*

Umbria (central, N of Rome)

Utopiaggia Villa Piaggia 21, I-05010 Montegabbione (Terni). ☎ 0763-87020. *20 ad, 15 ch, living in three houses; community moved there from Germany. 100 hectares, with sheep, goats, cattle, a horse and poultry; cheese production, pottery, other handicrafts; language courses. Consensus decision making; always looking for new members.*

Puglia (SE, Bari/Brindisi)

Fondazione Bhole Baba Casella Postale 138, I-72014 Cisternino (Brindisi). *Very spiritual; Indian-influenced guru ashram. Their guru is Babaji-Herakhan Baba.*

Calabria (far south, Reggio)

Comunità Agricola Cà Morosini Via del Pino No. 5, I-42030 Montalto (RE). ✳

••••••••••••••••••••••••••••••

Netherlands

Groningen

De Hobbitstee van Zijlweg 3, NL-8351 HW Wapserveen. *8 adults, 7 children; founded 1969, the oldest community in Holland. Rural, self-supporting, income-sharing. Ecology, non-violence, spirituality, personal growth.*

De Warkstee Spoorlaan 31, NL-9774 PC Adorp. ☎ 05090-1411.

Gelderland (Arnhem)

De Refter Rijstraatweg 37, NL-6574 AC Nijmegen-Ubbergen. *200 people in an old convent school.*

Utrecht

Emmaüs Haarzuilens Eikstraat 14, NL-3455 SJ Haarzuilens. *A ragpickers community. They collect used goods, sort and sell them. Profits are spent on Third World and other projects for the poor. 10 members; members are expected to work full-time and receive board, lodging, pocket-money, and full insurance.*

Zeeland (Vlissingen)

Tidorp Hogezoom 79, NL-4328 EL Burgh-Haamstede. *Working Buddhist community. Vipassana meditation.*

Noord-Brabant (Eindhoven)

Ark Gemeenschap De Weyst P. Peterusstraat 21, NL-5423 SV Handel. *Linked to the Communautés de l'Arche in France.*

••••••••••••••••••••••••••••••

Norway

Gateavisa Hjelmsgate 3, N-0355 Oslo 3. ☎ 22-69 12 84. *An anarchist group. Publish the magazine Gateavisa, with a circulation of 8000, spanning the entire range of alternative activities, and will have published a book about themselves called Gateboka. Since autumn 1992 they've run a phone service, Kotikatelefonen, with a focus on legal and illegal drugs. Their office is in an old three-storey wooden building which houses several other alternative services.*

Vidaråsen Landsby 3420 Andebu. *Camphill Community, about 170 people in 17 households.*

••••••••••••••••••••••••••••••

Poland

⚅ **Kuan Um School of Zen** Matowiejska 22/24, 04-962 Warsaw. ☎ Office tel/fax 15-05-52 (at night fax only). Head temple tel 15-04-00.

Gdansk Zen Centre Grunwaldzka 51/4, 80-241 Gdansk.

Krakow Zen Centre Smolki Str. 14/1, 30-503 Krakow.

••••••••••••••••••••••••••••••

Spain

Andalucia (far south)

Colectividad los Arenalejos Lista de Correos, E-29567 Alozaina, Málaga. *7 Ad 5 Ch; permaculture, hygiènisme, social ecology. "We work at relating* with children for a libertarian culture." Write in Spanish or French. Produce newsletter La Hoja.

Cooperativa Tierra y Libertad Lista de Correos, El Bosque, Cadiz. *Co-op of people used to being farm labourers who want to try to have some power for a change; sheep, poultry, cow, garden, olive trees and plenty of land to be developed.*

Alicante (SE)

La Mariola Lista de Correos CP, E-03800 Alcoy (Alacant). *Planned community; social ecology. Two people with goats.*

Leon (NW)

Mataveneiro E-24300 Bembibre. *Communal village; arts and crafts.*

Euskadi (Basque Country)

Lakabe Family/Community Valle de Arce, Lakabe, E-31438 Itoiz, Navarra.
Minas Iñaki, C / S. Sebastian no.10-4°, Izda Renteria (Gipuzkoa). *5 adults and a child in a squat; theatre, etc. Address given is contact address.*
Caserio Bikunieta Apdo de Correos No 51, Azkoitia Gipuzkoa. *5 adults; goats and lambs.*

Baleares

Palma Zen Centre C/ Sant Feliu 6, E-07012 Palma de Mallorca. ☎ (971) 728981. *A meditation centre of the Kuam Um School of Zen, under the direction of Zen Master Seung Sahn. They offer traditional meditation every week, and two intensive retreats every year.*

•••••••••••••••••••••••••••••••

Sweden

Iskcon Korsnäs Gard, S-14032 Grödinge. *Hare Krishna community, SW of Tumba on the Himmerfjarden, in an old manor, surrounded by hills and lakes. 20 adults, some children. "Up here we have a farm community, school for children, a few restaurants, sawmill, some shops, Food for Life programme, preaching centres, cooking courses, and most of all, we are publishing the old Vedic literature in different languages."*
Solicentrum Box 16, S-28072 Killeberg. *A Linbu community. Principles for society formulated in The Theory of Conscious Light by H. Linbu, who*

actively leads the community. *Practical application of esoteric wisdom. "We welcome all with good will, sincerity and a wish to work with us. We try to realise our dreams and for that we need to dig deep to gather!"*
Stjärnsund Stiftelsen Stjärnsund, S-77070 Långshyttan. ☎ +46 225 80001 or 225 80210. Fax 225 80301. *Findhorn-inspired community with fairly loose membership structure. Beautiful surroundings app 200 km NW of Stockholm. Residential courses all the year, working guest programme. Families welcome, hectic during the summer!*

•••••••••••••••••••••••••••••••

Switzerland

Longo Mai Missionstraße 35, CH-4002 Basel. *Linked to the Longo Mai community in France.*

NORTH AMERICA

There are many communal groups in North America, particularly in the United States. For more information do refer to the new edition of the US based Directory of Intentional Communities which is due out late autumn 1993. We hope to have them on sale by mail order from our Redfield address. The 1990/91 edition listed 290 communal groups in the States, 26 in Canada and two in Mexico, as well as a selection from elsewhere in the world. Here are five good resources in the USA:
Fellowship of Intentional Community PO Box 814, Langley WA 98260. ☎ (206) 221-3064. *General enquiries about communities, and publishers of Directory of Intentional Communities.*
Ambitious Amazons PO Box 811, East Lancing MI 48826. *Info on lesbian and women-only spaces. Their directory costs $4.*
RFD Route 1, Box 84-A, Liberty TN 37095. *Journal for radical faeries, focussing on alternative country living.*
Leaves of Twin Oaks Twin Oaks Community, Route 4, Box 169, Louisa VA 23093. *Journal of successful large*

income-sharing community. See articles on pages 23 and 75.

Community Bookshelf East Wind Community, Tecumseh MO 65760. ☎ (417) 679-4682.

LATIN AMERICA

Colombia

Atlantis Lista de Correos, Telecom, Tolima. *10 Ad 7 Ch; a noisy self-expressive hard-working group, matriarchal in the sense that pleasure, feelings, atmosphere, non-superficial communication and a well-stocked kitchen come first; grow coffee, sugar-cane, corn, bananas, European veg and South American crops; trying to buy chain-saw threatened forest around them. Visitors welcome. Up-to-date news from Peter Razzell, 21 Haringey Pk, London N8 (081 347 9860). He sells books about Atlantis written by Jenny James. Address at Tolima is contact address.*

Mexico

Krutsio Communidad Apartado Postal 174, Guerrero Negro, Baja California Sur. *They use Esperanto!* ❋

AUSTRALASIA

Australia

South Australia

🅘 **Cennednyss Community** (Don and Estelle Gobbett), P.O. Summertown, SA 5141. *11 Ad 6 Ch; five houses and 15 acres in the Adelaide Hills. Moora Moora mentioned Lionel Pollard (Willing Workers on Organic Farms contact), Mt Murrindal Reserve, W. Tree, via Buchan, Victoria 3885, as someone who has for some time maintained information about communities in Australia. There is a good magazine based around communities in Nimbin: Nimbin News, P.O. Box 209, Nimbin 2480. Another useful magazine is Grass Roots, Night Owl Publishers, Box 242, Euroa 3666.*

Hillier Park Hillier Road, Gawler, SA 5118. *Emissary community.*

Queensland

Coondoo Farm Co-op 10 Stuart Road, Mt Wolvi, via Gympie, Queensland 4570. *3 Ad 4 Ch; rural, new age healing centre planned.*

Crystal Waters Permaculture Village MS16, Malewy, QLD 4552. *Address given is contact address. See article on page 13.*

Mandala Mary Vale, MS 394, Warwick, Qld 4370. *25 Ad 8 Ch; rural, wildlife sanctuary.*

New South Wales

Billen Cliffs Pty Ltd POB 865, Lismore, NSW 2480. *75 Adults 45 Children; loose-knit, rural.*

Bundagen PO Repton, NSW 2454. *80 Ad 60 Ch; rural, permaculture, personal growth.*

Dharmananda Community The Channon, NSW 2480.

Koorool Community Candelo, NSW 2550. ☎ (064) 932 374; (064) 932 026; (064) 932 019. *Four families live on the farm on the edge of Tantawangalo State Forest and run whole-food shop in Bega.*

Lillifield Community Lillifield, Lillian Rock, NSW 2474. ☎ (066) 897 224; (018) 385 965.

Mount Oak Community PO Box 6, Cooma, NSW 2630. *25 Ad 3 Ch; rural, permaculture, personal growth.*

New Goverdhan . ☎ 066 724566 9am-1pm. *70 Ad 30 Ch; rural, food production, spiritual.*

Wyuna Community 22-24 Morant Circuit, Kambah, 2902 ACT, Canberra.

Victoria

Moora Moora PO Box 214, Healesville, Vic 3777. *14 km outside of Healesville. Estab. rural community of 20+ households on 230 ha mixed farm land and forest. Membership shares available, options to build or to buy an existing house. Registered primary school on the property and bus to take older children to schools. 40 Ad 30 Ch; rural, alternative technology.*

Commonground P.O. Box 474, Seymour, 3660 Victoria. *An income sharing community which uses consensus decision making and has an events centre; 7 Ad 5 Ch.*

Fusion Arts Colony POB 293, Mornington, Vic 3931. *15 Ad 5 Ch; rural and urban, Christian, vis arts.*

Mount Murrindal Co-op W. Tree, via Buchan, Victoria 3885. *6 Ad. rural; land reclamation; therapeutic.*

Ontos Natural Health Retreat via Buchan, Vic 3885. *12 Ad 8 Ch; rural, conservation, food production.*

Sunrise Farm W. Tree, via Buchan, Vic 3885. *18 Ad 6 Ch; rural organic farm, therapeutic.*

••••••••••••••••••••••••••••••

NZ/Aotearoa

North Auckland (N. Island, NW)

Centrepoint Community PO Box 35, Albany, Auckland 10. *About 130 residents; rural, income sharing, spiritual, personal growth.*

Nelson (South Island, NW)

Rainbow Valley Community McCallum's Road, Takaka, Golden Bay. ✸

Renaissance Community Graham Valley, RD1 Motueka, Nelson. ✸

Riverside Community RD2 Upper Moutere, Nelson. *38 Ad 35 Ch; rural, spiritual, income sharing, consensus decision-making; farm, apple orchards; about 500 acres, est 1941.*

Tui Community Wainui Bay, RD2 Takaka, Golden Bay. ✸

Canterbury (South Island, E)

Chippenham Commune Crickegrass, Woodside Road, Oxford. ✸

ASIA

India

Ⅱ **Mitraniketan Community** Mitraniketan PO, Vellanad 695543, Kerala. ☎ Vellanad 2045, 2015 or 2086. *About 100 Ad 300 Ch; farming, various arts, crafts, schools, publishing, promotion of ecological and environmental development, along with an exposure for international living. "We have a view to develop Universal Responsibility among people while working with people at local level. Our aim is a holistic approach to promote development."*

Aum Swarupa Community 1170/12 Revenue Colony, Pune 411 005.

Auroville Unity Village, Tamil Nadu 60 5101.

Infact Kizhathadiyoor P.O., Palai, Kottayam 686 574. *Collective facilitating other collective projects such as food co-ops, youth training, promotion of women's, environmental and health issues. Infact is short for Information for Action. May not be a community as such.*

NIRDA (National Integrated Rural Development Agency) Sithayan Kottai, Dindigul Anna Dist., Tamil Nadu 624 708. *May not be community as such.*

••••••••••••••••••••••••••••••

Japan

Yamagishi Association Toyosato Jikkenchi, 5010 Takanoo-cho, Tsu-shi, Mie-ken 514-22. *Contact point for Yamagishi Villages (about 40 in Japan, one each in Korea, Brazil and Switzerland), but not other places in Japan. Write in German, English, French, Portuguese, Chinese, Korean or Japanese. Yamagishi Villages are non-political, non-religious communities, where no money is needed. The largest has about 900 people.* ✸

••••••••••••••••••••••••••••••

Israel

Ⅱ **International Communes Desk** Yad Tabenkin Study Centre, Efal P.O., Ramat-Efal 52960. *Now re-activated, with information about kibbutzim in Israel and up-to-date info about communities all round the world. They publish the magazine Call, with international communes news in English. The kibbutz movement started in 1909, and there were 250 secular and 17 religious groups in 1992.*

AFRICA

Ghana

Rainbow Relief Foundation P.O. Box 673, Kaneshie-Accra. *Not a community, but organises workcamps to help with community farms.*

If this is the first *Diggers & Dreamers* that you've come across then you'll probably be interested in the earlier editions. Although the Directory information in both will obviously have been superceded they contain a wealth of interesting articles (often referred to in this edition).

Now readers of this book can obtain these earlier versions at a specially reduced price (while - as they say - stocks last!)

Diggers and Dreamers 90/91 (128 pp) contains articles on: Getting started; Decision making, childcare and celebration in community; Days in the lives of urban and rural communards; Cohousing; and a historical overview. **£2.50 including postage and packaging** *reduced from the previous mail order price of £5.75*

Diggers and Dreamers 92/93 (216 pp) contains the following: Communes Network?; How not to rock the boat; New communities; Changing and growing; A future for alternative lifestyles?; 19th century Communalism; Whiteway; Garden cities and green villages; Community offspring; Running a business in a community; HIV/AIDS; Guidelines for co-operative living. **£3.50 including postage and packaging** *reduced from the previous mail order price of £8.00*

Cheques should be made payable to "Diggers & Dreamers" and sent to Diggers and Dreamers, Redfield Community, Winslow, Buckinghamshire MK18 3LZ. Please indicate clearly which edition(s) you require.

The Editorial Team

Chris Coates *Born 1957. Anarchist , Clown, Pyro-sculptor & Quantum mechanic. Long term member of People in Common. Involved in running ecological timber co-op, property renovation, caring for 13 year old son, local arts and community politics.*

Jonathan How *Born 1953. Keen on databases, design and developing strategies. At Redfield since 1984. Likes the first days of Spring and heading in a south-westerly direction.*

Lee Jones *Born 1940. Has been a single parent, a journalist and a social worker. Is now a community mediator. A founder member of the Quaker Community at Bamford where she has lived for the past five years. Involved in the building (in both its meanings) work there.*

William Morris *Born 1961. Has lived at Ritherdon Road and Lifespan (three times). Designs and writes the annual Lifespan Lunar Tree Calendar. Important to him are the moon, the sea, sunbathing nude, Star Trek: TNG, and the support of his lovely friends. Works for the future of the Edward Carpenter Community.*

Andy Wood *Born 1957. Involved with communal projects since 1979. A member of the Greentown Group, now living at Rainbow Housing Co-op. Has also undertaken academic research about communal life at the Co-operatives Research Unit of the Open University.*